CUTTING EDGE

EGA

INTERMEDIATE

WORKBOOK

Longman

jane comyns carr   frances eales

Contents

Introduction

	PAGE
Grammar terms	4
Using a dictionary	5

Module 1

Making questions	6
Short answers	6
Question tags	7
Present Simple or Continuous	7
Word order: adverbs of frequency	8
Pronunciation: /ə/ (schwa) / the letter 's'	9
Grammar snack: *both* / *neither*	10
Vocabulary: activities with *do* / *play* / *go*	11
Improve your writing: spelling of the *-ing* form	11
Listen and read: unusual lifestyles	12

Module 2

Past Simple or Continuous	13
Pronunciation:	14
syllable stress in Past Simple forms	
used to	14
still, not any more* / *longer	15
Listen and read: Frankenstein	16
Grammar snack:	17
articles (first and second mention)	
Vocabulary: scientists and technologists	17
Improve your writing:	18
spelling of Past Simple forms /	
using *when* / *while* / *as* / *during* / *for* in stories	

Module 3

Comparatives and superlatives	20
Comparative and superlative adverbs	21
Comparing things in different ways	22
Vocabulary: places around town	22
Grammar snack: prepositions of place (*at, in, on*)	23
Pronunciation: /ð/ and /θ/	23
Improve your writing:	23
punctuation (capital letters)	
Grammar snack: the definite article (places)	24
Improve your writing: postcards	25

Module 4

	PAGE
Present Perfect Simple and Past Simple	26
Present Perfect + *just* / *yet* / *already*	27
for*, *since* and *ago	27
Present Perfect Continuous	28
Grammar snack: articles with *school*, *college*, etc.	28
Vocabulary: describing people's appearance	29
Pronunciation: /ɪ/, /iː/ and /aɪ/	30
Listen and read: Tom Cruise	30
Improve your writing: punctuation (commas)	31

Module 5

will* and *won't	32
going to	32
Present Continuous for future arrangements	33
Other ways of talking about the future	33
Future clauses with *if, when,* etc.	34
Grammar snack:	35
prepositions of time for the future	
Pronunciation: /ɜː/, /ɔː/ and /əʊ/	35
Vocabulary: jobs / adjectives to describe jobs	36
Real life: formal telephone conversations	37
Improve your writing: apostrophes	37

Module 6

***-ed* / *-ing* adjectives**	38
Grammar snack:	38
prepositions after *-ed* / *-ing* adjectives	
The passive	39
Vocabulary: films, TV and newspapers	40
Grammar snack: .	41
prepositions for talking about books, films, etc.	
Pronunciation: /f/, /v/ and /w/	41
Listen and read: letters fo a TV magazine	42
Improve your writing:	43
linking ideas without repeating yourself	

Module 7

	PAGE
Polite requests	44
Ways of making offers	45
will **(instant decisions and responses)**	46
Jazz chant (*go*)	47
Grammar snack: articles (making generalisations)	47
Listen and read: food from other countries	48
Vocabulary: food and cooking	49
Pronunciation: lost letters	50
Improve your writing:	50
sending and replying to invitations by e-mail	

Module 8

Defining relative clauses	51
Prepositions with defining relative clauses	52
Quantifiers (*a few, a lot of*, etc.)	53
Grammar snack:	54
articles with countable / uncountable nouns	
Vocabulary: formation of nouns	54
Pronunciation: /ʒ/, /ʃ/, /dʒ/ and /tʃ/	55
Reading	55
Improve your writing:	56
formal and informal styles	

Module 9

Futures for prediction (*will, might, may*, etc.)	57
Hypothetical possibilities with *if*	58
Real and hypothetical possibilities	58
If **sentences in social situations**	59
Grammar snack: word order	59
of adverbs (*certainly, probably, definitely*)	
Vocabulary: money verbs and prepositions	60
Improve your writing: opening a bank account	61
Listen and read: lottery winners	62
Pronunciation: /ʌ/	62

Module 10

	PAGE
Past Perfect or Past Simple	63
Present Perfect or Past Perfect	63
Reported statements	64
Reported questions	64
say **and** *tell*	65
Vocabulary: weather phrases	65
Listen and read: Sherlock Holmes	66
Pronunciation: connected speech (links	67
between words)	
Grammar snack:	67
definite article for shared knowledge	
Improve your writing:	68
time expressions for telling stories	

Module 11

Obligation and permission	69
Obligation and permission in the past	70
must **and** *have to*	70
make **and** *let*	71
Spelling and pronunciation:	71
school / university subjects	
Vocabulary: transport (noun + noun)	72
Grammar snack:	72
prepositions of movement	
Grammar snack: *-ing* forms as nouns	74
Improve your writing: linking words	74

Module 12

could have / should have / would have	75
Past sentences with *if*	76
Grammar snack: verb + object + infinitive	77
Jazz chant:	77
verbs that describe behaviour and reactions	
Vocabulary:	78
using the dictionary (revision)	
Real life:	79
starting and finishing conversations	
Improve your writing:	80
a letter to sort out a problem	

Answer key	81

Introduction

Grammar terms

(a) Doctor, doctor, please help me. I <u>can't</u> stop <u>telling</u> <u>lies</u>.

I <u>don't</u> believe you.

HOW TO BE HONEST

(b) Doctor, doctor, people <u>never</u> notice me!

Next, please.

(c) Doctor, doctor. I'm worried <u>because</u> I think I'm getting smaller.

Well, you'll just have to <u>be</u> <u>a</u> little patient.

(d) Waiter, this bowl is <u>wet</u>!

That's <u>your</u> <u>soup</u>, sir.

(e) How did <u>you</u> find <u>the</u> chicken, madam?

I looked <u>under</u> the peas.

1 Look at these grammar terms and complete the gaps with one of the underlined words from the jokes above.

a   a countable noun *lies*

b   an uncountable noun ....

c   an adjective ....

d   a preposition ....

e   an adverb ....

f   the base form of the verb ....

g   the -ing form of the verb ....

h   an auxiliary verb ....

i   a modal auxiliary verb ....

j   a definite article ....

k   an indefinite article ....

l   a pronoun ....

m   a possessive adjective ....

n   a conjunction ....

Using a dictionary

2 A dictionary can be very useful to find the grammar of a word. Look at these two extracts from the *Longman Active Study Dictionary* and complete the gaps below.

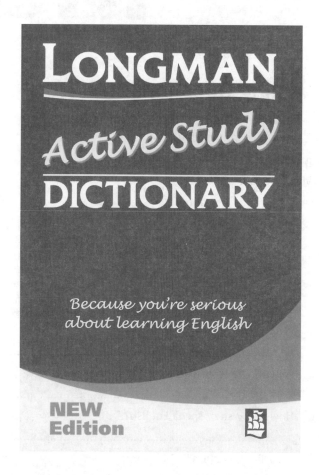

Abbreviations			
adj	adjective	*prep*	preposition
adv	adverb	*pron*	pronoun
v	verb	*n*	noun

en·joy /ɪnˈdʒɔɪ/ *v* [T] to get pleasure from something: *Did you enjoy the movie?*| **enjoy doing sth** *My Wife really enjoys playing golf.*

enjoyment *n* [U] *We hope the bad weather didn't spoil your enjoyment.*

en·joy·a·ble /ɪnˈdʒɔɪəbəl/ *adj* giving you pleasure: *We all had an enjoyable afternoon.*

train² /treɪn/ *v* [T] to teach someone how to do something, especially the practical skills they need to do a job: *Staff are trained in how to deal with difficult customers.*

train·ee /ˌtreɪˈniː/ *n* [C] someone who is being trained for a job: *a trainee teacher*

train·er /ˈtreɪnə/ *n* [C] someone whose job is to train people how to do something

train·ing /ˈtreɪnɪŋ/ *n* [U] when someone is taught the skills they need to do something: *a training course*

a   enjoy is *a verb*

b   enjoyment is ....

c   enjoyable is ....

d   train is ....

e   trainee is ....

f   trainer is ....

g   training is ....

3 Complete each gap with one of the words from exercise 2.

a   Where did Jenny *train* .... to be a ski instructor?

b   My father gets a lot of .... from his garden.

c   I really .... spending time on my own.

d   How much football .... do you do every day?

e   The course was really .... I recommend it.

f   Patricia's only a .... chef, but her cooking is fantastic!

g   Our .... wants us to finish our project this week.

module 1

Making questions

1 Use the prompts to write complete questions in the following situations.

a) Steve is asking Phil about his new girlfriend, Cinzia, who comes from Italy.

1 What / be / her name?
What's her name ....?

2 Which part of Italy / she / come from?
....?

3 How / you / meet / her?
....?

4 What / she / do for a living?
....?

5 When / she first / come / to England?
....?

6 How well / she / speak English?
....?

7 she / like / London?
....?

8 she / have / a flat here?
....?

b) Sarah wants to emigrate to Australia with her family. An official is asking her some questions.

1 When / you / get married?
....?

2 Where / your husband / born?
....?

3 your husband / work?
....?

4 he / have / any qualifications?
....?

5 How many children / you / have?
....?

6 How old / be / your children?
....?

7 you / know / anybody in Australia?
....?

Short answers

- *Do you like rock music?* | Yes, I like rock music. **Yes, I do.**

- *Did you enjoy the film?* | No, I didn't enjoy the film. **No, I didn't.**

The long answer is unnatural, so we use a short answer.

2 Look at these long answers. First write the questions and then write a short answer for each one.

a No, I'm not married.
Are you married ....?
No, I'm not ....

b Yes, I live with my family.
....?
....

c No, we don't live in an apartment.
....?
....

d No, we didn't live in the same place when I was young.
....
....?
....

e No, my grandparents aren't alive.
....?
....

f No, I haven't got a car.
....?
....

g Yes, I can understand English well.
....?
....

h No, my English teacher doesn't speak my language.
....?
....

Question tags

- *He's got* her phone number, *hasn't he?*
  +　　　　　　　　　　　　 **−**
- *It isn't* very warm today, *is it?*
  −　　　　　　　　　　　　 **+**

Notice:

1 *You take* sugar in your coffee, *don't you?*
　　↑　　　　　　　　　　　　　　↑
　no auxiliary　　　　　　　auxiliary *do*

2 *I'm really early, aren't I?*
　　　　　　　~~amn't I?~~

3 **a)** Complete the gaps in these sentences with a question tag.

1) Two friends are shopping:

a Ooh, it's cold today, *isn't it* ....?

b That coat costs a lot, ...?

c They've got some nice clothes here,
.............?

d These jeans are too short, ...?

e There aren't many sales assistants here,
.............?

2) Mrs Halliday is talking to Liesbeth, who has come to stay for six months and help with the children:

a You're from Amsterdam, ...?

b You speak French, ...?

c You've got two little brothers, ...?

d You don't smoke, ...?

e You can drive, ...?

b) 🔊 Listen to the statements and add the correct question tag.

You hear:　　　　　　**You say:**

Ooh, it's cold today, ...　　*Ooh, it's cold today, isn't it?*

Present Simple or Continuous

4 Mike, a salesman, is talking to his doctor about his stress problems. Complete the gaps with the best form of the verb in brackets.

DOCTOR: How can I help you, Mr Daniels?

MIKE: Well, I started having bad headaches a couple of weeks ago and they (1) *'re / are getting* .... (*get*) worse. I can't sleep properly, I'm tired all the time, and the worst thing is my hair (2) .... (*go*) grey and I'm only 31!

DOCTOR: I see. Let me ask you some questions. (3) .... (*you / smoke*)?

MIKE: No, I gave up a month ago.

DOCTOR: Right. I see you're a salesman. On average how many hours a week (4) .... (*you / work*)?

MIKE: Well, I normally (5) .... (*do*) eight hours a day, but at the moment I (6) .... (*work*) at least ten hours and some Saturdays.

DOCTOR: That is a lot. And so how (7) .... (*you / relax*)?

MIKE: Well, I usually (8) .... (*sit*) in front of the TV with a pizza and a few beers.

DOCTOR: Hmm. (9) .... (*you / do*) any exercise at the moment?

MIKE: Not really, but I'm losing a lot of weight and I (10) .... (*not / know*) why.

DOCTOR: I think you (11) .... (*suffer*) from stress. I (12) .... (*want*) you to eat a more varied diet and to do some exercise. Come back and see me in four weeks and I'll check you again.

State verbs

5 The following conversation takes place in a camera shop. Complete the gaps with the best form of the verb in brackets.

A: Good morning, how can I help?

B: Well, I (1) *I'm looking* (look for) a compact camera with a 200m lens.

A: Right. Well, this new model's very good. It (2) .... (have) a zoom and a built-in flash and it only (3) .... (cost) £150.

B: Ah. You see I (4) .... (buy) it for a friend and he (5) .... (not / want) to spend more than £100.

A: OK, I (6) .... (understand) the problem. Let's see – I (7) .... (think) the Zenco 460 is a very good buy. There's a picture here in the catalogue.

B: Oh, yes, that (8) .... (look) nice.

A: The only problem is that we (9) .... (not have) any in the shop at the moment. In fact, we (10) .... (wait) for some to come from our other shop in Oxford.

B: Right, so when will they be here?

A: Well, I (11) .... (not know) exactly. I really need to ask the manager, but I'm afraid she (12) .... (have) lunch at the moment. She'll be back in about half an hour.

B: OK. Perhaps I'll come back later.

Word order

Adverbs of frequency

> **LOOK!**
>
> Some adverbs come before the main verb, but after the verb *to be*:
>
> | I | always nearly always | do my homework. |
> |---|---|---|
> | I'm | quite often sometimes occasionally hardly ever never | late for class. |
>
> Some adverbs go at the beginning **or** end of the sentence:
>
> | **Most of the time** | I do my homework | **most of the time.** |
> |---|---|---|
> | **Sometimes Occasionally** | I'm late for class | **sometimes. occasionally.** |

6 **a)** Rewrite these sentences with the adverb in the correct position (there may be more than one correct answer).

1 I speak English on the phone. (*sometimes*)
   I sometimes speak English on the phone .

2 My colleague Jo uses my computer. (*occasionally*)
   ....

3 My classmate Carla has lunch with me. (*quite often*)
   ....
   ....

4 My boss is in the office. (*hardly ever*)
   ....

5 My neighbours are very quiet. (*most of the time*)
   ....
   ....

6 My sister-in-law Jenny phones me on Mondays. (*nearly always*)
   ....
   ....

7 Paul's relatives visit us at Christmas. (*always*)
   ....

8 Stephen sees his ex-girlfriend. (*hardly ever*)
   ....

9 Daryl, my flatmate, cleans the bathroom. (*never*)
   ....
   ....

b) Write five sentences in your notebook about how often you do things. Show them to your teacher.

Pronunciation

/ə/ (schwa)

> **LOOK!**
>
> • *husband* has 2 syllables: husband
>   /ə/
>
> • *acquaintance* has 3 syllables: acquaintance
>   /ə/   /ə/
>
> In *husband* 'hus' is stressed (it is stronger and longer) and 'band' is unstressed (it is weaker and shorter). In *acquaintance* the second syllable is stressed and the first and third syllables are unstressed.
>
> We often pronounce the unstressed syllable /ə/.

7 a) Notice where the stress falls in the words below. Which sounds are pronounced /ə/? Write the symbol underneath.

1 economy
  /ə/

2 step-mother

3 couple

4 brother-in-law

5 photograph

6 stranger

7 relative

8 foreign

9 headteacher

10 neighbour

11 partner

12 parent

b) Listen and repeat the words, paying attention to the stress and /ə/ sound.

c) Listen and mark the stress and /ə/ sound(s) on the following words.

1 often
  /ə/

2 occasionally

3 usually

4 assistant

5 salesman

6 catalogue

The letter 's'

> **LOOK!**
>
> The letter 's' can be pronounced /s/ /z/ or /ɪz/ in:
> • plural forms of nouns:
>   *flatmates*, *neighbours*, *marriages*
>   /s/   /z/   /ɪz/
> • Present Simple, third person singular:
>   *she smokes*, *he learns*, *it increases*
>   /s/   /z/   /ɪz/

8 a) Listen to the nouns and verbs in the box (or say them aloud) and complete the chart below.

wants nieces spells entertains practises parents acquaintances relatives uses classmates colleagues hopes works spends pronounces

/s/	/z/	/ɪz/
wants		

b) Listen again and repeat the words.

Grammar snack

both / neither

9 **a)** Carl is studying English in Edinburgh. His friend Julie is studying Psychology at Bath University. Read these extracts from their letters to each other and decide which of the statements below are correct.

Julie

... I'm really enjoying the course, although I have a lot of work to do in the evening, apart from Fridays and Saturdays, when I go dancing or to a pub. I'm glad that I came to Bath University – the city is really beautiful. The university is on a hill just outside the city, and there is a bus service, but I usually cycle, which takes about an hour. Actually, I'm getting quite fit, because I go jogging most mornings. How are you getting on in ...

Carl

... and my teacher gives us homework nearly every day, so I spend at least an hour doing that in the evening, before I go out. I usually go to a pub – the pubs here in Edinburgh are always busy and the people are really friendly. I met a Scottish boy in a pub soon after I arrived and – guess what – we go fishing together every Sunday. My only problem now is that I have a long journey by bus to school every morning. I think I'll start looking for new accommodation nearer to school ...

1 a They both have a lot of work to do. ✓
  b Carl has a lot of work, but Julie doesn't.

2 a Julie is doing a lot of exercise, but Carl isn't.
  b They are both doing a lot of exercise.

3 a Neither of them go dancing at weekends.
  b Julie goes dancing at weekends, and Carl goes fishing.

4 a Neither of them go to pubs.
  b Both of them go to pubs.

5 a Neither Carl nor Julie live near their school / university.
  b Both Carl and Julie live near their school / university.

b) Correct these sentences.

1 My ex-girlfriend and I (liked) both travelling.

2 Neither my neighbours are noisy.

3 Both my sister and my niece spends a lot of time cooking.

4 My colleagues Dan and Rob are quite lazy: neither of them doesn't do much work.

5 My best friend June and I both are learning a musical instrument.

6 Neither Ann and Susan likes watching football.

c) Write five sentences about your friends / colleagues / classmates / family with *both* and *neither*.

1 ....
....

2 ....
....

3 ....
....

4 ....
....

5 ....
....

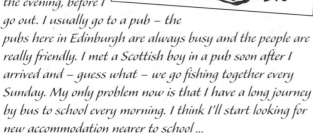

LOOK!

Notice the position of *both* in these examples:

• *They **both** have a lot of homework.*

• *They are **both** students.*

• ***Both** of them are studying.*

Notice the forms we can use with *neither*:

• ***Neither** of them work / works.*

• ***Neither** Carl **nor** Julie live / lives ...*

• ***Neither** Carl **nor** Julie doesn't live ...*

Vocabulary

Activities with *do* / *play* / *go*

10 **a)** Put the activities in the box into the correct column in the chart below (six for each verb). Mark the stress on each word.

the drums   sport   photography   cycling   swimming   gardening
the guitar   cards   knitting   exercise   snooker   a computer game
yoga   jogging   skiing   dancing   volleyball   walking

do	play	go
		• cycling

b) 🖅 Listen to the prompts and say the correct verb.

You hear: ... the drums

You say: play the drums

LOOK!
- We use *play* for musical instruments and games with rules.
- We use *go* for hobbies and sports, especially when we have to go somewhere to do them (with expressions such as *a lot of*, *a bit of*, *some / any* we can use *do*: '*I do a lot of walking*').
- We use *do* for other hobbies (often creative hobbies).

c) Match these questions and answers and complete the gaps with the correct form of *do*, *play* or *go*.

1 That's a lovely jumper. Where did you get it?

2 Where are the children? They're very quiet.

3 Do you .... a lot of exercise?

4 Would you like to .... dancing?

5 How did you learn to .... the drums?

6 Do you know much about cameras?

a I think they're .... a computer game.

b No, but ask John; he .... a lot of photography.

c I taught myself.

d Not really – but I .... swimming occasionally.

e Oh, my grandmother made it. She *does*........ a lot of knitting.

f I'd love to. When?

1 ..*e*..   2 ....   3 ....   4 ....   5 ....   6 ....

Improve your writing

Spelling of the *-ing* form

LOOK!
To make the *-ing* form, we usually add *-ing* to the base form of the verb: *sleeping*, *reading*, *opening*.

There are three exceptions:
- One-syllable verbs, e.g. *put*, where there is a single vowel '*u*' and then a consonant '*t*', we double the final consonant: *putting*. (We never double x, y or w: *boxing*, *buying*, *knowing*.)
- Verbs which end in a single *-e*, lose the *-e*: *make – making*.
- These three verbs (with two syllables) double the final consonant: *forget – forgetting*, *begin – beginning*, *travel – travelling*.

11 Spell the *-ing* form of these verbs.

a read *reading*.........

b pay ....

c write ....

d see ....

e begin ....

f fax ....

g hope ....

h plan ....

i jog ....

j travel ....

k print ....

l answer ....

m train ....

n grow ....

o drive ....

Listen and read

Unusual lifestyles

12 a) 🔲 Three people are talking about their lifestyles. Read and / or listen to the texts. What are their jobs?

Gemma

'I absolutely love music and listen to it all the time, even when I go jogging. Of course I have to look after my voice. I do exercises for three hours every day and I take lots of vitamin C. If I get a sore throat I go straight to bed and rest. I usually try to get at least eight hours sleep a night anyway. ... As for my job – you really can't be shy in this kind of work, and you have to be very patient because sometimes we practise for hours before we get it right. When we're on tour, we work for several weeks with no breaks and you can get really tired. For relaxation, whenever I get a holiday, I go straight to a sunny beach, but the thing I enjoy the most is the great feeling you get from a live audience.'

1   Gemma is a / an

....

2   Raoul is a / an

....

3   Frank is a / an

....

Raoul

'Well, my work's really quite stressful. Most people think you spend your day chopping vegetables and stirring soup, but it's not that simple. You have to be really careful with the food and keep everything very clean. The big problem is my boss – he shouts at me all the time – even, for example, if I forget to wash up one plate – I just can't do anything right sometimes. Actually, I'm hoping to find a new job soon because I don't get much time off. I'd like to have more weekends free, to see friends and to spend more time with my two little boys. You know it's strange spending all day with food – when I go home I just want to eat a sandwich or a bag of chips and I'm terribly critical when I eat in a restaurant.'

Frank

'Well, I first got interested because I loved doing them so much myself – I used to do at least one every day. I suppose I've got the right kind of mind really – I enjoy playing around with puzzles, especially word puzzles. So I sent a couple in to a local newspaper and was really surprised when they asked me for more. I suppose it is a strange way to spend your day – surrounded by dictionaries and books, but it's great that I can organise my own time, so I try to finish by two and then I can take my dog for a walk. It's very satisfying though – I love the feeling after I've thought of the final clue, and it all fits together. It's also really nice when people write to me and thank me. Funny really, because I'm just doing what I like.'

b) Read and / or listen again, and answer these questions: Who:

1   works with food? *Raoul* ....

2   isn't happy in their job? ....

3   spends a lot of time reading? ....

4   is careful about their health? ....

5   has a logical mind? ....

6   likes being in front of lots of people? ....

7   has two sons? ....

8   has free afternoons? ....

9   practises a lot? ....

10 has a very strict boss? ....

module 2

Past Simple or Continuous

1 Choose a phrase from each box to make a complete answer for the questions below.

I was peeling some onions and
She was travelling home from work and she
We were sunbathing at the weekend and we
They were staying in Florida when
He was walking in the rain and he
He was playing football and he

got very wet.
stayed out too long.
the knife slipped.
left it on the bus.
fell over.
there was a terrible storm.

a How did you cut your finger?
I was peeling some onions and the knife slipped .

b How did Tony hurt his knee?
....

c How did you all get so sunburnt?
....

d How did Martin catch a cold?
....

e How did a tree fall on the Simpson's car?
....

f How did Sara lose her bag?
....

2 Complete the gaps in these dialogues with the best form of the verb in brackets.

A: I phoned you last night at 8.00 but you didn't answer. What (1) *were you doing*............ (you do)?

B: I (2) .... (work) on my computer and I (3) ....(not hear) the phone ring. Sorry!

A: Good Morning. International Chemicals Incorporated. May I help you?

B: Hello, yes I (4) .... (talk) to the Financial Director a minute ago and the line (5) .... (go) dead.

A: Oh, I'm sorry, Madam. I'll reconnect you.

A: When did you meet your husband?

B: When I (6) .... (be) in Canada last winter.

A: Were you on holiday?

B: No, I (7) .... (train) to be a ski-instructor, but on the second day I (8) .... (break) my leg. I (9) .... (spend) eight weeks in hospital and he was my doctor!

3 Use the prompts to write two conversations about accidents. Choose the best form of the verb.

a A: Penny told me you / have / accident yesterday. What / happen ?
Penny told me you had an accident yesterday.
What happened .... ?

B: We / drive / home and another car / stop / suddenly and we / go / into it.
....
....
....

A: Be / the other car alright?
.... ?

B: Yes, luckily we / not / go / very fast.
....
....

13

b   A: How / your brother get that scar / his hand?

....

....

....?

B: He / get / it / while we / live / in Italy.

....

....

....

A: Oh, how?

B: He / play / near the oven and he / burn / his hand on the oven door.

....

....

....

A: Ooh, nasty!

Pronunciation

Syllable stress in Past Simple forms

4 a) How many syllables do these *-ed* forms have? Mark the stressed syllables ● and the unstressed syllables ○.

● ○	
1 happened	9 practised
●	
2 stopped	10 decided
3 travelled	11 improved
4 looked	12 received
5 reminded	13 repeated
6 watched	14 started
7 asked	15 closed
8 changed	

b) 📼 Listen to the verbs in phrases and repeat them.

used to

5 Read the text and mark the sentences below *T* (true) or *F* (false). Underline the words in the text which help you decide.

Recently a Russian friend came to visit me. It was one of her lifelong dreams to visit London, and she certainly knows more about the city than I do. She arrived at lunchtime and we spent a tiring afternoon going round the Tower of London. However, by 5 o'clock I couldn't help noticing that she didn't seem as enthusiastic as she had been earlier. I asked if anything was wrong and she said, 'This is all very interesting but where is the fog and where are the men in bowler hats? Why did everyone push to get on the bus at the bus stop instead of making a queue? It's very different from the books I've read about England.'

Her comments made me think. It's true that people don't queue much any more: nowadays you often find that everyone just jumps on the bus. Or maybe this is only in London. Also the idea of a man standing up and offering his seat to a woman on a train or bus is unusual these days, although my father still does it!

As for the weather: well, we all know that a hundred years ago there used to be fog all year round in London, but we no longer have much fog; nowadays we have pollution from all the cars! Over the last few years in the summer London has been one of the hottest places in Europe, although we still get more than enough rain in the other seasons.

What about the city men in their working 'uniform'? Well, you can still see some city 'gents' in their smart suits, but men hardly ever wear bowler hats. A few things don't change, though. If you try to start a conversation with an English person on the underground in London, she or he will probably look at you as if you are mad!

a   Everything was as she expected it to be. ..*F*..

b   People don't queue as much as they used to. .....

c   Men used to give up their seats to women on public transport. .....

d   It still rains a lot in winter. .....

e   Most London businessmen no longer wear bowler hats. .....

f   People used to talk to each other on trains and still do. .....

6 Linda's life has changed a lot in the past ten years. Write six sentences about the changes using *used to* and *didn't use to* (the words in brackets will help you).

LINDA TEN YEARS AGO

LINDA NOW

a (*smoke*) *She used to smoke* .

b (*hair*) ....

c (*car*) ....

d (*boyfriend*) ....

e (*smart clothes*) ....

f (*unhappy*) ....

still, not any more / longer

LOOK!

When we use *still, not any more / longer* in a *used to* sentence we often use an auxiliary verb instead of the main verb:

• *I used to have a bicycle but I **don't** any more / longer.*
• *I used to like the Beatles and I still **do**!*

When we use the verb *to be* + adjective, we don't repeat the adjective:

• *I used to be fat but I'm not fat any more.*

7 Reorder the words in these sentences. The first word is underlined.

a doing – still – used – and – <u>I</u> – do – to – sports – hate – I
I used to hate doing sports and I still do .

b to – she – any – be – <u>Jo</u> – shy – used – isn't – more – but

....

....

c Bob – play – they – <u>Tim</u> – and – used – still – football – do – to – and

....

....

d used – he – longer – to – for – any – <u>Peter</u> – work – Mrs Warren – but – doesn't

....

....

e make – to – does – laugh – used – and – still – <u>Sam</u> – me – he !

....

....

f more – boyfriend – me – he – to – chocolates – <u>My</u> – used – any – buy – but – doesn't

....

....

Listen and read

Frankenstein

8 **a)** 📼 What do you know about the story of Frankenstein? Here is an extract from the beginning of the story. A man named Victor Frankenstein has gone to university to study science. At first he writes frequently to his friends and family, then the letters stop. His close friend Henri (the narrator of the story) goes to visit him. Read and / or listen to the text and answer the questions.

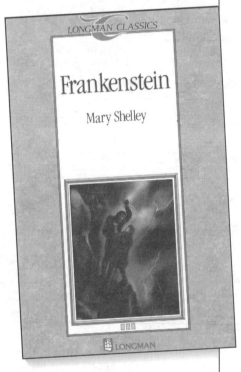

1 How do you think the narrator (Henri) feels at the end of the extract?

2 How does Frankenstein feel?

3 What was in the bath?

b) Here is a diagram of Frankenstein's flat. Label the diagram using words from the box.

window bed bath table
living room passage
work-table

1 Frankenstein led the way down a long, dark passage to a book-filled room. A bed stood on one side, looking as if nothing had been done to it for days; and on a table near the window were the remains of several meals. There was dust everywhere, and
5 the last of the evening sun shone with difficulty through the dirty windows. There was a rather unpleasant smell.

After I had given him news about his family and told him the reasons for my coming to Ingolstadt, Frankenstein got up and walked about the room excitedly. He didn't seem to be thinking
10 at all about what I had just told him.

'Henri,' he said at last. 'You have come just at the very moment when I need your help. The great work which I have been doing for the last year is coming to an end, and I shall soon know whether I have been wasting my time or whether I have
15 pushed scientific discovery to new heights.' His eyes burned with a strange light. They were like the eyes of a madman.

'My preparations are nearly complete. All I need now are the right conditions for the great experiment to take place. Come,' he said, and led the way to a door in a corner of his living-room.
20 'You will see what no other man has seen.'

He threw open the door, and at once the strange smell which I had noticed before became stronger. It was like the smell of bad meat. I could hardly bear it, but my friend seemed not to notice it, and led the way in.

25 The room was dark, and at first I could only see a mass of wires, glass bottles and jars, and copper and glass pipes. Here and there the blue light of the burners made holes in the darkness. And from those places the sound of boiling liquids could be heard.

30 As my eyes began to see better in the half-darkness I saw that this stuff was arranged round a kind of bath in the middle of the room with a wooden work-table that went all the way round it. Frankenstein was watching me. There was still this strange excitement in his eyes. 'Go on,' he said, 'look inside. See what I
35 have made.'

I bent over the table and looked into the bath. It was filled with a clear liquid. I tried to see deeper into the liquid, but at first all I could see was what looked like hair – fine hair. I bent lower, and as Frankenstein moved a lamp nearer I drew in my
40 breath sharply. It *was* hair – spread out in a golden ring around a face, a head. More. Yes, there was a body in the bath – the body of a man!

window

Grammar snack

Articles: first and second mention

> Notice how *a/an* and *the* are used in the Frankenstein extract:
>
> 'Frankenstein led the way ... to *a* book-filled room ... Frankenstein got up and walked about *the* room ...'
>
> • *a* is used the first time we mention something.
> • *the* is used when we mention something for the second (third, fourth, etc.) time.

9 a) Read paragraphs five (He threw open ...) and eight (I bent over ...) of the Frankenstein extract. Circle seven more examples of this use of *the*. Draw an arrow to show what *the* refers back to.

b) Below is a summary of what happens next in the story. Complete the gaps with a/an or the.

Frankenstein has made (1) .*a*.... man and he's waiting for (2) .... storm so that he can do (3) .... experiment and bring (4) .... man alive with the help of lightning. Henri helps him with (5) .... experiment and they succeed. However, (6) .... man is (7) .... monster, ugly and horrible, and Frankenstein chases him away.

Shocked and disappointed, Frankenstein gives up his studies and goes back to his family home in Geneva. Henri decides to follow (8) .... monster because he is worried about what it might do next. He discovers that it has gone into a forest and made friends with (9) .... blind man and his children. When Henri visits (10) .... forest several weeks later, he finds (11) .... man's house burnt to the ground. Soon after this, he hears that Frankenstein's little brother has been murdered and his nurse is going to be hanged for the crime.

Worried that (12) .... monster is responsible for the child's death, Henri rushes to Geneva, but neither he nor Frankenstein can stop the hanging. They decide to look for (13) .... monster in the mountains and it comes to meet them with (14) .... request. As it tells them (15) .... request, Frankenstein and Henri learn that (16) .... monster was kind at first, but because people were disgusted by its ugly looks, it became more and more cruel. 'What I want now is a wife as ugly as I am.'

Vocabulary

Scientists and technologists

10 a) The people below all work in science and technology. Which subject does each one study? Complete the words.

1 a mathematician   ma _thematics_
2 a scientist   sc _ _ _ _ _
3 a doctor   me _ _ _ _ _ _
4 a psychologist   ps _ _ _ _ _ _ _ _
5 an engineer   en _ _ _ _ _ _ _ _
6 an architect   ar _ _ _ _ _ _ _ _ _
7 a geologist   ge _ _ _ _ _

b) The following sentences describe what each person does in their job. Circle the correct verb(s) in each sentence.

1 A scientist *does* / *makes* experiments and *carries out* / *makes* research.

2 A psychologist *investigates* / *looks* people's problems.

3 A doctor *cares* / *treats* patients and *tells* / *gives* advice.

4 An architect *draws* / *writes* plans of buildings.

5 An engineer *carries out* / *executes* tests on roads and bridges.

6 A mathematician *makes* / *finds* calculations.

7 A geologist *looks* / *takes* rock samples and *proves* / *analyses* them.

Improve your writing

Spelling of Past Simple forms

11 **a)** Look again at the rules for spelling the *-ing* form on page 11 of the Workbook. The rules are the same for spelling the Past Simple form (ending in *-ed* not *-ing*). Complete the chart below.

	-ing form	Past Simple
stop	*stopping*	*stopped*
train	....	....
plan	....	....
look	....	....
fax	....	....
phone	....	....
offer	....	....
travel	....	....
allow	....	....

> **LOOK!**
>
> Verbs ending in a consonant + *y*, change *y* to *i* and add *-ed*:
> • *cry – cried*.
>
> Verbs ending in a vowel + *y* don't change the *y*:
> • *pray – prayed*.
>
> Note: There are two exceptions:
> • *say – said, pay – paid*.

b) Write the past form of these verbs.

1 try *tried* ....
2 enjoy ....
3 hurry ....
4 play ....
5 pay ....
6 employ ....
7 stay ....
8 dry ....
9 apply ....

Using *when* / *while* / *as* / *during* / *for* in stories

> **LOOK!**
>
> When we talk about actions or situations that take place at the same time, we can use *when* / *while* / *as*:
> • *Maggie hurt her leg **when** / **while** / **as** she was jogging.*
> • *I was talking to Penny **when** / **while** / **as** you were playing tennis.*
>
> If we are talking about a single event at a particular time, we can only use *when*:
> • *Jane was sixteen **when** she first met David.*
>
> Look at these examples using *during* and *for*:
> • *I'm staying with my cousin **during** the holidays.* (part of the holidays)
> • *I'm staying with my cousin **for** the holidays.* (the whole of the holidays)
>
> Note: we use *during* / *for* with nouns.

12 **a)** Below is part of a letter that Jenny wrote to her brother, describing her terrible week. Cross out any words you cannot use.

... And then on Thursday, I took a new client out for lunch at that French restaurant in the centre of town. What a disaster! Everything was fine at first – we got a nice table, but (1) when / as / while / during / for they started playing music, we found we were next to the speakers. We changed tables and ordered our meal. We waited (2) when / as / while / during / for 30 minutes before the waiter brought the wine, and then, (3) when / as / while / during / for he was pouring it, he spilt it all over my client's suit.

She said, 'Don't worry,' but I could see she was very angry, so (4) when / as / while / during / for we were having the first course, the atmosphere was quite tense. Then (5) when / as / while / during / for we were waiting for the main course, the couple on the next table started having a loud argument!

The worst thing was (6) when / as / while / during / for the bill came, I realised I'd left my credit card at home. I felt really embarrassed and in the end she had to pay. And that wasn't all – I said goodbye to her and went to the car park and found someone had stolen my car radio (7) when / as / while / during / for the meal.

b) Alan is talking about his weekend. On Saturday he went to his friend Kyra's party. Another friend, Guy, had offered to take him to the party by car. Complete the gaps with *when / while / as / during* or *for*.

Well, I was getting dressed (1) *when* .... Guy rang and said he was ill, so I decided to go by train. Unfortunately, (2) .... I was talking on the phone, the cat walked over my clean shirt, so I had to find another one and I was late leaving.

(3) .... I was walking to the station it started snowing and I got very cold. I just missed a train and I had to wait at the station (4) .... half an hour. (5) .... the train finally arrived I was

frozen! I was so cold and tired that (6) .... the journey I fell asleep and I missed my station.

Well, I got off at the next stop and decided to walk back to Kyra's. I walked (7) .... half an hour and then I realised I was lost. Luckily I found a phone and telephoned for a taxi. (8) .... I finally arrived at Kyra's house it was nearly midnight and people were going home. What a terrible evening!

Comparatives and superlatives

1 Sean wants to celebrate his birthday at a nightclub. He's got information from three clubs in the city. Complete the gaps in the conversation below with the best form of one of the adjectives from the box.

Paradiso
Dance to 'Los Gitanos'
£10 entrance
Maximum 150 people
Dress:
no jeans please
Only 10 minutes from the centre

All Nite Long
DJ Max plays your favourite rock & pop
£7 entrance
Maximum 250 people
IN THE CITY CENTRE

LIAM'S PLACE
Smokey Joe's Jazz Band
£8.50 entrance
Maximum 75 people
Dress: jacket and tie
Only 15 minutes from the city train station
LIAM'S PLACE

quiet cheap good central expensive far successful big crowded friendly

SEAN: I think *All Nite Long* looks good: my friends haven't got much money and it's (1) ....*the cheapest*.......... of the three places. It's also
(2) ...., they can take 250 people, and it's
(3) .... so people could get there easily.

MEERA: But *Paradiso* has (4) .... music than *All Nite Long* – they don't have real bands there.

JUSTIN: Actually, I think you should go to *Liam's Place*: I know it's
(5) .... away than the other two, but because it's small, it has a (6) .... atmosphere: the big clubs are too impersonal. Also, it's much (7) .... if people want to talk.

MEERA: Well, *Paradiso* isn't noisy at all. I know it's (8) .... nightclub in town, but for £10 you get live music and a great atmosphere.

JUSTIN: But you know it's much (9) .... than *Liam's Place*: you often can't get a table.

MEERA: Well that's because it's (10) .... club in the northwest at the moment – everyone wants to go there.

SEAN: Hold on! It's *my* birthday, remember, and I want ...

2 You want to rent a place to live. You went to see a house and a flat and made these notes. Correct the sentences below with a word or phrase from the box (there is one wrong word in each sentence). More than one answer is possible.

House	Flat
– rent: £600	– rent: £575
– no. of rooms: 8	– no. of rooms: 3
– 45 minutes from station	– 40 minutes from station
– very quiet location: no traffic	– on a busy main road – very noisy!
– not at all clean	–very clean
– furniture: fine	–furniture: terrible!

a bit   a lot   much   slightly   a little

a little / slightly / a bit
a The house is much more expensive than the flat.

b The flat is a bit smaller than the house.

c The flat is much closer to the station than the house.

d The house is a little quieter than the flat.

e The flat is slightly cleaner than the house.

f The furniture in the flat is a bit worse than the furniture in the house.

Comparative and superlative adverbs

LOOK!

Most adverbs that end in *-ly* form the comparative with *more* and the superlative with *most* (NB: **not** *the most*):

• *Could you speak **more clearly** please?*
• *You can find it **most easily** by turning right.*

The following adverbs are the same as the comparative and superlative forms of adjectives.

fast	- faster	- fastest	hard	- harder	- hardest
early	- earlier	- earliest	far	- further	- furthest
late	- later	- latest	well	- better	- best
long	- longer	- longest	badly	- worse	- worst

3 a) We often use comparative forms of adverbs in requests. Read these sentences and complete the requests.

1 You can't hear what your teacher is saying.
Could you *speak more loudly please* ....?

2 Your teacher's writing is difficult to read.
Could you ....?

3 You're going to the airport in a taxi and the driver's going very slowly.
Could you ....?

4 Someone's teaching you to use a computer but they explain very quickly.
Could you ....?

5 Your friend usually comes to work or school with you at 8.00 in the morning. Tomorrow you want him to come at 7.30.
Could you ....?

6 Your friend rings, but you are watching your favourite TV programme.
Could you ....?

7 You are visiting your grandmother in hospital. She doesn't want you to leave yet. What does she say?
Could you ....?

b) 🔊 Listen to each situation and say the request.

You hear: You can't hear what your teacher is saying.

You say: *Could you speak more loudly please?*

21

Comparing things in different ways

4 Look at the following sentences and make one complete sentence, using the word in **bold**.

a   A meal in the Four Seasons restaurant costs £15. A meal in the Pizza Parlour costs £11.
less
A meal in the Pizza Parlour costs *less than a meal in the Four Seasons restaurant* .

b   The Manor Hotel is £50 a night. The Park Hotel is £75 a night.
expensive
The Manor Hotel isn't ....
....

c   Savewell supermarket has 2000 customers a day. Pricerite supermarket has 1500.
more
Savewell supermarket ....
....

d   It takes 40 minutes to cross the city by bus. It takes 25 minutes to cross the city by bike.
less
It takes ....
....

e   There are three trains an hour in the afternoon. There are five trains an hour in the morning.
fewer
There are ....
....

f   The furniture in my sister's flat is more or less the same as Tim's.
similar
The furniture in my sister's flat ....
....

g   The Guggenheim Museum in Bilbao is made mostly of metal. The Guggenheim Museum in New York looks like a concrete multi-storey car park.
different
The Guggenheim Museum in New York ....
....

h   Phil's flat has four rooms and a balcony. My flat's opposite his, and it's got four rooms and a balcony, too.
same
My flat's ....

Vocabulary
Places around town

5 **a)** Find eight more words in the word square for places around town (the words go across and down). Use the clues below to help you.

A	N	T	I	Q	U	E	S	H	O	P	B
C	A	O	G	R	N	D	B	K	S	G	C
E	R	S	J	A	U	F	Q	I	T	B	O
S	T	A	D	I	U	M	T	L	A	F	N
H	G	L	M	C	K	D	G	R	T	P	C
T	A	X	I	R	A	N	K	N	I	B	E
J	L	P	B	O	E	O	H	A	O	D	R
F	L	O	R	I	S	T	S	C	N	J	T
N	E	E	D	F	R	I	B	M	E	F	H
D	R	Y	C	L	E	A	N	E	R	S	A
G	Y	C	I	A	H	K	A	E	S	G	L
S	H	O	P	P	I	N	G	M	A	L	L

1   You take your dirty clothes here for cleaning if you don't want them to get wet: *dry cleaners*

2   You can buy pens, paper and files here:
    s _ _ _ _ _ _ _ _

3   You could see a football match or a pop concert here:
    s _ _ _ _ _ _

4   You can buy and send flowers from here: f _ _ _ _ _ _ _

5   A place where taxis wait together: t _ _ _   r _ _ _

6   You can spend a morning or an afternoon looking at an exhibition here: a _ _   g _ _ _ _ _ _

7   A place to listen to an orchestra playing classical music: c _ _ _ _ _ _   h _ _ _

8   If you buy a present here, it will definitely be old and might be expensive: a _ _ _ _ _ _   s _ _ _

9   Lots of shops together, in a covered area:
    s _ _ _ _ _ _ _   m _ _ _

b) 🔊 Listen to the words and mark the main stress: e.g. dry cle·aners.

c) 🔊 Listen to the words in phrases and repeat them.

Grammar snack

Prepositions of place: *at*, *in*, *on*

> **LOOK!**
>
> When we think about a place as a point, we use *at*:
>
> •
>
> • *There's someone **at** the door.*
> • *You have to change trains **at** Dublin.*
>
> We use *on* to describe the position of something on a surface:
>
> ——•——
>
> • *I think your keys are **on** that shelf.*
>
> We also use *on* when we think about a place as a point on a line:
>
> ——•——
>
> • *Budapest is **on** the river Danube.*
>
> We use *in* when something is in a three-dimensional space:
>
> • *He's **in** the bathroom.*

6 Complete the gaps in the text below with *in*, *on* or *at*.

Rosaria lives (1) ...*in*... Salerno, (2) .... Italy. It's a port (3) .... the south-west coast. She lives (4) .... the city centre (5) .... Via Nizza No 244, (6) .... a huge apartment (7) .... the top floor of a modern building. Her family live very close to her: her sister and brother-in-law live (8) .... the end of her street and her mother lives (9) .... the next street. Rosaria works for an advertising company: her office is (10) .... Corso Vittorio Emanuele, the main shopping street. It's not too far away, so she walks there every day and stops (11) .... her way to have breakfast (12) .... a local café.

Pronunciation

/ð/ and /θ/

7 🔊 **a)** Listen to the words in the box (or say them aloud) and complete the chart below.

the thin theatre another there thank you
these that third both brother through

/ð/	/θ/
the	*thin*

b) 🔊 Listen to these sentences and repeat them.

1 The theatre's over there.
2 Thank you for these.
3 Both of my brothers are thin.
4 There's another room through there.
5 That's the third one I've seen.

Improve your writing

Punctuation: capital letters

> **LOOK!**
>
> We use a capital letter for:
> • people's initials and names, their marital status and job title: *Ms F. Green, Personnel Manager*.
> • the names or initials of companies: *International Chemicals, IBM*.
> • the names of places: *New Zealand, Park Road*.
> • languages, nationalities and religions: *Tom speaks Chinese, a Greek statue, Sue's a Buddhist*.
> • days, months, and public holidays: *Christmas Day is on Wednesday the 25th of December*.
> • the most important words in titles of books, magazines, films, etc.: *Empire of the Sun*.

8 Find and correct any mistakes in the following sentences.

a I'm meeting professor Allinton on Tuesday Afternoon, aren't I?

b Do you know any good japanese restaurants? Our Managing director, Mr Hashimoto, is coming over next week.

c *Twenty thousand leagues under the sea* was written by jules verne.

d What are you doing at easter?

Grammar snack

The definite article: places

9 **a)** 🔈 Read and /or listen to the 'jazz chant', paying attention to the rhythm.

Where shall we go for our summer vacation?

Europe or Asia or closer to home?

We could try the Bahamas or maybe Jamaica

Go round the UK, or Denmark or Spain.

We could sail the Pacific or even Lake Como

Or go down the Yangtze as far as Shanghai.

Or maybe we ought to try something exciting

Like climbing Mount Fuji or crossing the Alps.

I've got a suggestion: what's wrong with New York?

We could see Brooklyn Bridge and sit in Times Square,

Watch a movie on Broadway and walk down Fifth Avenue.

Central Park's great if the weather stays fine.

Then we'll pick up a taxi from Grand Central Station

To JFK Airport and catch our flight home.

That's what I'd like for my summer vacation –

No mountains or beaches but plenty of fun!

b) Put the places in the box into the correct column in the chart. Find an example (or examples) from the 'jazz chant' for each place.

| continents   groups of islands   single islands |
| republics or unions of states   countries |
| oceans or seas   lakes   rivers |
| single mountains   mountain ranges |
| cities / towns   roads / streets / avenues |
| squares   bridges   parks   stations   airports |

with *the*	without *the*
	continents: Europe, Asia

c) Complete the gaps in the holiday advertisement with *the* if it is necessary.

Winter Breaks with Sunspot Holidays

Visit (1) .... Australia!

❋ Spend the first three days in (2) .... Sydney

❋ See (3) .... Sydney Harbour Bridge

❋ Go shopping in (4) .... George Street

❋ Visit (5) .... Blue Mountains, just outside the city.

❋ Then go north to (6) .... Whitsunday Islands and practise your diving in (7) .... Pacific Ocean.

❋ Finally, see the crocodiles from the film *Crocodile Dundee* in (8) .... Kakadu National Park.

This is a once in a lifetime offer! Fourteen days that you'll never forget.

❋ **Call 010 600 4000 now.**

Improve your writing
Postcards

When writing postcards, we often leave out a lot of words to save space:

- ~~We're~~ having a great time...
- ~~The~~ food is wonderful ...

10 **a)** Read postcard A from New York and decide where the words in the box should go. What types of words are usually left out?

The	there	are	my	is	~~We're~~
We're	We'll	be	The	is	We

Dear Pete and Sarah,

We're
↖having a great time here in the Big Apple. Weather brilliant – hot and sunny. Spent most of today shopping – fantastic department stores here: credit card's not looking too healthy! Hoping to do some sightseeing tomorrow – 5th Avenue, Times Square, etc. Nightlife also incredible ... nobody seems to go to bed!

Back in a couple of weeks,
          love Sue and Joe
          XXXX

Mr and Mrs Hall,

3 Park Grove,

Leicester,

England.

Ⓐ

b) Read postcard B from Rome and circle the words which can be left out.

Dear Sam and Julie,

(We) arrived here a couple of days ago – the hotel is small but comfortable, but the food is not great. We're going on a tour of the whole city tomorrow, then we're planning to try some typical pasta dishes for dinner. We hope your family are all well, we'll see you in September.

          Love Mark and Tim

Sam and Julie Foster,
School Cottage,
Broadwood,
Gloucester,
England.

Ⓑ

c) Imagine that you are on holiday. Write a postcard to an English-speaking friend.

module 4

Present Perfect Simple and Past Simple

1 Read this interview with Zoe, a singer in a pop group, and circle the best verb form.

I = Interviewer   Z = Zoe

I: Well, it's nearly Christmas and your single's number 1 in the charts. You must be very pleased.

Z: Oh yes, of course: (1) *it was /it's been* an incredible year for us – we (2) *already had / 've already had* two number 1 songs this year and (3) *we did / we've done* a tour of the UK.

I: OK, tell us how it all (4) *started / has started*.

Z: We only (5) *formed / have formed* the group in January, and since then we (6) *spent / 've spent* almost every day together. At first we only (7) *played / have played* other people's songs and we (8) *didn't start / haven't started* writing our own songs until we (9) *found / 've found* our manager, Brian.

I: Uh huh … so when (10) *was / 's been* your first big concert?

Z: Well, that was in May, and around the same time Brian (11) *helped / 's helped* us to get a recording contract with Sony.

I: Yes, and your album's doing very well in the charts. So what's next?

Z: Well, we're working on some new songs and we (12) *agreed / 've agreed* to do a US tour next summer.

I: Great! Well, we all wish you the best of luck and thank you for coming on the programme.

2 Six of the sentences below are wrong. Find the mistakes and correct them.

a   <u>Have ~~you seen~~</u> the news last night? *Did you see*

b   Carrie's a really close friend – we knew each other for ages.

c   I've had this cold all week.

d   Hello, er … sorry, I forgot your name.

e   Jeff's never broken a promise before.

f   Oh, that's a nice watch. How long did you have it?

g   My secretary was late for work every day last month.

h   Look! It's stopped raining!

i   I see your team's in the final. Did they ever win the cup?

j   We didn't play tennis together since the summer.

k   Have you seen John this morning? We've got a meeting together at 11.30.

l   I can't find my keys – has anyone seen them?

3 Read this extract from an article called *Famous Mums and Dads* and complete the gaps with the best form of the verb in brackets.

'It (1) *was* .... (be) my birthday yesterday: I'm 14 years old. Some people say I'm lucky but I don't think so. Imagine, in my life I (2) .... (go) to eight different schools and I (3) .... (never stay) anywhere long enough to make a best friend. We (4) .... (live) in so many different houses that I can't remember some of them. In fact, last year we (5) .... (move) house three times. It's true, there are some good things: I (6) .... (meet) some really famous people and we (7) .... (have) some great holidays – I (8) .... (go) to Disneyland at least four times, but never with mum and dad. When I (9) .... (be) young, I always (10) .... (have) a nanny, and she (11) .... (take) me on holiday. I'm staying with my aunt and uncle at the moment because my dad's making a film in France and my mum (12) .... (go) to Los Angeles.'

Present Perfect + *just / yet / already*

LOOK!

Notice the position of *just* and *already*:
• John's **just** arrived.
Just = a short time before now.

• 'Would you like a sandwich?' 'I've **already** eaten, thank you.'
Already = before now and means sooner or earlier than we expected.

• 'Have you seen that film **yet**, Tim?'
• Jill hasn't been to the British Museum **yet**.
Yet = before now. We often use *yet* when we **expect** that the person we are talking about **will** do something. It is used in questions and negatives.

4 Reorder the words in these sentences. The first word is underlined.

a film – I – started – the – already – has – think
I think the film has already started .

b haven't – my – yet – homework – I– done
....

c just – married – They – got – 've
....

d Mark – of – come – hospital – yet – Has – out ?
....

e brother – a – just – My – has – car – bought – new
....

f Christmas – all – already – Jane – sent – cards – has – her
....

5 **a)** Match a sentence from column A with one from column B to make a dialogue.

A	B
1 Have you phoned Brian yet?	a Yes, we've already met.
2 You look great.	b I've already done them.
3 Do you want a drink?	c No, I haven't had any food yet.
4 What did you think of the video I gave you?	d Thanks, I've just come back from holiday.
5 Do you know Susie?	e No thanks, I've already had four beers.
6 Have you tried this pizza? It's really good.	f I haven't had time to watch it yet.
7 Could you finish those letters by lunchtime?	g He's just gone out.
8 Have you seen John?	h Yes, but he wasn't in.

1 ..*h*.. 2 .... 3 .... 4 ....
5 .... 6 .... 7 .... 8 ....

b) Now cover up column B. Say the first line of the dialogue aloud and try and respond with the second line.

for, since and *ago*

6 Complete the gaps in these sentences with the words in brackets and either *for, since, ago* or nothing (–) in some sentences.

a Joy's had toothache
for three days .
(three days)

b Frankie last went to the dentist
....
(six months)

c My brother and I started going jogging
....
(a year)

d Jane's been feeling sick
....
(last night)

e I took two aspirins
....
(this morning)

f Pete's been on a diet
....
(two weeks)

g I haven't done any exercise
....
(months)

h We played football
....
(all day yesterday)

i I've been doing aerobics
....
(this time last year)

j My mother hasn't been feeling well
....
(her operation)

27

Present Perfect Continuous

7 Circle the best verb form in the following sentences.

a I've been knowing /(I've known) Susan for about five years.

b Mum had to take Tim to the dentist because he's *been breaking / broken* his tooth.

c My husband*'s been having / 's had* his mobile phone for a week and it isn't working.

d I hope Karen rings soon because Rick*'s been waiting / 's waited* by the phone for hours.

e We've *been going / gone* to the new sports centre since June. Why don't you come and try it?

f Giuseppina's English is getting much better. She*'s been practising / 's practised* a lot recently.

g You look much slimmer. Have you *been dieting / dieted*?

h John's boss *has been deciding / has decided* to have a holiday next month.

i Goodbye and thanks for having us. We've *really been enjoying / enjoyed* this evening.

j TEACHER: Ok. *Has everyone been finishing / Has everyone finished* the exercise? Fine. Let's go on.

Grammar snack

Articles with *school*, *college*, etc.

> LOOK!
>
> A *Matt went **to school** in Kansas.*
> B *His father went **to the** school to see the head teacher.*
>
> In sentence A Matt is a student and goes to school to study, which is the usual reason (no article).
>
> In sentence B the father is visiting the school building, he doesn't study there (we use *a* or *the*).
>
> Here is another example:
> • *Nelson Mandela spent many years **in prison**.*
> • *His wife couldn't go **to the prison** very often to visit him.*
>
> Places that follow this rule are: school, college, university, hospital, church, court, prison.

8 Look at these sentences and cross out *the* or *a* when they are not necessary.

a 1 My sister has been in ø̷ hospital since her operation.

2 I phone the hospital every morning to see how she is.

b 1 'Where's Billy?' 'He's still at the school: his lessons don't finish until 4.00.'

2 There's a school very near here.

c 1 I waited in the church for the rain to stop.

2 'Do you go to the church?' 'Yes, every Sunday.'

d 1 Jan's going to the court today because she hasn't paid her taxes for five years.

2 Tourists are allowed to visit the court on Thursday mornings.

e 1 I left the university when I was 21.

2 My parents came to the university for my graduation day.

f 1 My three years at a college were fantastic.

2 I went to the college to see an exhibition.

Vocabulary

Describing people's appearance

9 a) Complete the chart below with a word or phrase from the box and *he's*, *he's got* or *he wears*.

> smart   a rather pointed nose   quite slim   of medium build   going grey
> quite wavy   not very tall   friendly   casual   a bit overweight   round
> sparkly eyes   highlighted   good dress sense   colourful   going bald

Face	Clothes	Build	Hair
He's ... *got a rather* *pointed nose*	*He ...* *wears smart* *clothes*	*He's ...*	*He's / His hair's ...*

b) Complete the gaps in these descriptions with words and phrases from the boxes.

1   My uncle Bill's ....*quite tall*................ . He's got grey, curly hair and a ...., ... face. He often wears very .... and he always looks quite ....

> friendly   round   colourful clothes   smart   quite tall

2   My grandmother's .... and she's a little .... She's got a .... face and white .... hair. She's getting a bit old now, but she always wears .... and she's got the most beautiful hands I've ever seen.

> smart clothes   wavy   overweight
> not very tall   friendly

3   My cousin Jim's 18. He's .... and not .... He's got long, ... hair and quite a .... face. He likes wearing .... clothes: jeans and t-shirts, usually.

> of medium build   very tall
> pointed   wavy   casual

c) In your notebook write a description **either** of someone famous **or** of someone in your class. Show it to your teacher.

Pronunciation

/ɪ/, /iː/ and /aɪ/

> **LOOK!**
>
> Compare these three sounds:
>
> /ɪ/: *a bit* *a biscuit*
>   /ɪ/   /ɪ/ /ɪ/
>
> /iː/: *to read* *people*
>   /iː/   /iː/
>
> /aɪ/: *my*   *white*
>   /aɪ/   /aɪ/

10 **a)** 🖭 Listen to the phrases below (or say them aloud) and write the correct symbol in the spaces.

1 his hair's quite thick
        /aɪ/   /ɪ/

2 he's medium build
      / /   / /

3 she's got green eyes
         / / / /

4 her hair's highlighted
        / / / /

5 she's pretty and very slim
       / /   / /

6 she's got a sweet smile
          / /   / /

7 he's kind and rather shy
      / /   / /

8 he's much thinner now he's in
    his teens   / /
        / /

b) Listen to the phrases again and repeat them.

Listen and read

Tom Cruise

11 🖭 Read and / or listen to this biography of the film star Tom Cruise and mark the statements below *T* (true) or *F* (false).

Born in Syracuse, New York on 3rd July 1962, Tom Cruise had a difficult childhood. His parents divorced when he was twelve, and in the first eleven years of his life his family moved a total of seven times. He had problems at school, partly because he never stayed in one place long enough to make friends and partly because he suffered from dyslexia and found reading very hard. As a teenager he couldn't decide whether to become a priest or a wrestler, but at the age of eighteen he chose acting as a career.

His first film *Endless Love*, in 1981, was followed quickly in the same year by *Taps* in which he had a strong supporting role as an angry young cadet. Over the next few years he made a name for himself in a series of fairly successful films often playing attractive 'boy-next-door' types. His big break came in 1986 in the hit *Top Gun,* where he played a rebellious fighter pilot with a killer smile.

By the late 1980s magazines were calling him 'easily the most powerful star of his generation' because of his more serious roles in *Rain Man*, in 1988, opposite Dustin Hoffman, and *Born on the Fourth of July*, which was made in the following year. For this film he received his first Oscar nomination for Best Actor for his powerful performance as the anti-war hero Ron Kovic. People who have worked with him say he's a perfectionist, preparing carefully for each role, and focusing 100 per cent whilst in the studio. Success continued in the 90s with films such as *Mission*

Impossible and *Eyes Wide Shut.* He is now one of the few actors who receives more than 20 million dollars a picture.

Cruise is a very private man, who rarely gives interviews. His personal life has had its ups and downs. In 1987 he married actress Mimi Rogers who was several years older than him, but the marriage ended in divorce in 1990. In the same year he married his co-star from *Days of Thunder*, red-headed actress Nicole Kidman. Both of them are members of the Church of Scientology, but Cruise has always refused to answer questions about his religion.

Whatever happens in his private life, people will remember him as one of the most charismatic actors of modern cinema and many will probably agree with *People* magazine in 1997 when they chose him as one of the fifty most beautiful people in the world.

a Tom Cruise was very successful at school. ..*F*..

b He always wanted to become an actor. .....

c He played the star part in *Taps*. .....

d *Top Gun* was his most successful early film. .....

e He was nominated for an Oscar for *Born on the Fourth of July*. .....

f He is a very hard worker. .....

g He hardly ever gives interviews. .....

h He got married to Nicole Kidman in 1991. .....

Improve your writing

Punctuation: commas

> **LOOK!**
>
> We put a comma (,) in a sentence to show a short pause.
>
> In a list, we use a comma instead of *and* or *or*:
> - *He lived in France, Italy, Belgium and Spain.*
>
> When we join two short sentences with a conjunction, e.g. *and*, *but* or *so*, we often use a comma before the conjunction:
> - *He moved to France, but he never forgot his friends in England.*
>
> If the sentence is short, a comma is not always necessary:
> - *He loved Paris but I didn't.*
>
> Notice where we put the commas in direct speech:
> - 'I'll buy the tickets,' he said.
> - She said, 'It's okay, I've got lots of money.'

12 **a)** Insert commas where necessary in these sentences.

1 I'm not very keen on jazz⊙ blues or rock music.

2 Steve practises his guitar every day and has guitar lessons twice a week.

3 I don't know much about the Beatles but I like their music a lot.

4 I like going to rock concerts but the tickets can be really expensive so I don't go often.

5 'I thought they were rubbish' Naomi said as we came out of the concert.

6 There were four members of the group: John Paul George and Ringo.

7 Jorge said 'You can borrow my guitar.'

8 'Come on' Paddy said 'or we'll be late.'

9 'I can get tickets for the 12th 13th or 15th January.'

10 The music was very loud but quite good.

b) In the following extract Bob Geldof, a famous rock star, talks about his meeting with Mother Teresa of Calcutta. Read the text and insert commas where necessary.

We sat in the airport till Mother Teresa came in. I felt hot⊙ tired and a bit nervous. I wanted to kiss her when I met her but she didn't let me. She told me about her work in Ethiopia. She and her sisters took care of sick people and homeless children. I wanted to help them and I told her about my music.

Then I said 'I'll give a concert in India for you.'

'No. God will give us what we need.' She turned to one of the important people nearby.

'I saw two big old palaces in the city' she said. 'Will you give me them for my homeless children?'

'I'm not sure about palaces but we can find you a house.'

'Two houses' said Mother Teresa.

'Two houses.'

I understood that Mother Teresa could ask for anything and she would get it. She was all goodness. She wanted nothing for herself. Then she took my hand and said 'I can do something you can't do and you can do something I can't do but we both have to do it.'

module 5

will and won't

1 Complete the gaps in these sentences with *will* or *won't* and a verb from the box.

> take   get   like   ~~be ready~~   come   be   need
> agree   pass   send

a I need these shoes on Saturday.
Will they be ready .... (they) by then?

b You can invite your ex-girlfriend to the party, but
I'm sure she ....

c We .... to order the flowers at
least two weeks before the wedding.

d .... (you) late tonight?

e I don't think you should buy Mum those gloves, she
.... them.

f So, the exam's in June. When ....
(they) us the results?

g Don't forget to take a sweater: I expect it
.... cold later.

h Stop worrying about the exam – you
.... easily.

i Why do you want to leave so early? It
.... very long to get there.

j You can ask her to type your work but I don't think
she ....

going to

2 Complete the gaps in these conversations with the correct form of *going to* and a suitable verb where necessary (short answers may be possible).

a A: It's my 18th birthday in June.

B: *Are you going to have* .... a party?

A: I haven't decided yet.

b A: My brother's just heard that he's lost his job.

B: Oh no! What .... ?

A: I think he's planning to travel for a while.

c A: Are you really going
to give up smoking?

B: Yes, ...
I threw my last packet
of cigarettes away
yesterday.

d A: Have you got any plans for the weekend?

B: Well, David and I ....
a film on Sunday night.

A: Oh, which one?

e A: Are you nervous about
making a speech at the
wedding?

B: Yes, but ....
....
about it any more.

A: No – thinking about it
will make you more
nervous.

f A: Lisa's really in love with Alain, isn't she?
.... him?

B: I hope so. He'd be the perfect husband for her.

g A: I heard that the council have bought that land
behind the cinema to build on.

B: Oh really? What ....
there?

A: A new shopping mall, I think.

h A: Are you and Annie going to have a holiday this
year?

B: No, ... We've got
no money.

Present Continuous for future arrangements

3 **a)** Who do the diaries below belong to? Choose from the box.

> a university student   a politician   a business person
> a dentist   a pop singer

A ....   B ....

TUESDAY 8TH

9.00	Mrs Philips, Ben & Sally – check up
10.00	Mr Lord – extraction
11.00	
12.00	Susan Kennedy
1.00	
2.00	
3.00	afternoon off
4.00	
5.00	

TUESDAY 8TH

10.30	Shakespeare lecture
12.00	Daniella – lunch
1.00	squash with Paul
3.00	meeting with Professor Livesy to discuss essay

b) Use the prompts to make complete sentences with the correct form of the Present Continuous.

Diary A

A: Hello, Mr Haines' surgery.

B: Yes, hello ... could the dentist see my daughter? She's got terrible toothache.

A: Well, he / see / patients all morning.

(1) _Well, he's seeing patients all morning_ ....

B: Um ... what about the afternoon?

A: I'm sorry, he / have / the afternoon off, but he could see you at 1 o'clock.

(2) ....

B: Oh thank you, I'll bring her then.

Diary B

C: I need to talk to you. Can we meet sometime today?

D: Well, I'm quite busy: I / go / to a lecture this morning and I / meet / Daniella for lunch.

(3) ....
....

C: What / you / do in the afternoon?

(4) .... ?

D: Well, I / play / squash until 3.00, then I've got a meeting.

(5) ....

you / do / anything in the evening? I'm free then.

(6) ....

C: No, that's fine.

Other ways of talking about the future

4 Use the prompts to make complete sentences in these dialogues.

a   My nephew Justin's leaving school in July.
Oh, what / he / intending / do / after that?
Oh, what is he intending to do
after that .... ?

b   What time are your grandparents coming?
They / due / arrive / at about six.
....
....

c   I'm going to spend the summer in Turkey.
Really? Where / you / planning / stay?
....
.... ?

d   I hear you've bought a new house.
Yes, we / hoping / move / next month.
....
....

e   Jeannie looks a bit worried.
I know, she / about / take / her driving test.
....
....

f   What are you going to do with the money you won in the lottery?
Well, I / thinking / buy / a new car with some of it.
....
....

g   Matt's been practising the piano a lot, hasn't he?
Yes, he / determined / win / the competition.
....
....

Future clauses with *if*, *when*, etc.

5 Match a question from column A with an answer from column B to make a dialogue.

A

a Will you call me tonight?

b Could you let Sandra have the plane tickets next week?

c Have you finished writing those invitations?

d Can you ask Tim to photocopy these letters?

e Is Jack coming to the party?

f What time do you expect to be home?

g Have you got the new *Oasis* CD?

h Could I borrow your tennis racket?

i Was your friend hurt in the accident?

B

1 He'll try to come if he's free.

2 Not yet, I'll finish them once I find my pen.

3 I don't know yet, I'll know more after I phone the hospital.

4 Yes, I'll phone you as soon as I get home.

5 Yes – I won't need it until the weekend.

6 Of course, I'll post them to her when I get them.

7 I'll be on the six o'clock train unless the meeting finishes late.

8 Yes. I'll make sure he does it before he goes home.

9 Yes, it's great. I'll play it for you next time you come to my house.

a ...4...   b ....   c ....   d ....   e ....

f ....   g ....   h ....   i ....

6 Look at these sentences and make one complete sentence, using the word in bold.

a We're going to play again. I'll beat you then.
   next time

   I'll beat *you next time we play* .

b You'll be in Madrid again. Phone me then.
   when

   Phone me ....

   ....

c It's going to get dark soon. Let's stop now.
   before

   Let's stop ....

   ....

d I'm moving house next week. Then I'll give you my phone number.
   after

   I'll give ....

   ....

e That film will come out soon. I'd like to see it then.
   as soon as

   I'd like ....

   ....

f Maurizio'll finish university soon. He hopes to get a job then.
   once

   Maurizio hopes ....

   ....

g The taxi'll come in a few minutes. I'll wait with you.
   until

   I'll wait ....

   ....

Grammar snack

Prepositions of time for the future

> LOOK!
>
> We use *on* with days and dates:
> * *I'm seeing him **on*** | *Tuesday afternoon.*
> | *the 6th of February.*
>
> We use *in* for a period longer or shorter than a day.
> * *We'll finish it **in** November / the afternoon / 2001.*
>
> We use *in* for a period between now and a future time:
> * *We're meeting **in** two days' time.*
>
> We use *at* for points in the future and holidays:
> * *We'll stop **at** midnight.*
> * *I'm going to see my parents **at** Easter.*
>
> There is no preposition with *next, this* or *the*:
> * *This time next week I'll be on holiday.*
> * *I'll finish my course the year after next.*

7 **a)** Look at the expressions in the box and put them into the correct column in the chart below.

> a few minutes   the year after next   2010   Saturday night   Sunday
> this time next year   midday   December 1st   a fortnight   Christmas
> next month   a moment   lunchtime   7.30   three weeks' time
> this time tomorrow   my birthday   next Saturday   a month's time
> Wednesday evening   the day after tomorrow

in	on	at	–
a few minutes			

b) Complete these sentences so that they are true for you (talking about the future).

1 This time tomorrow ....

2 On Saturday night ....

3 On my birthday ....

4 At 8 o'clock tomorrow morning ....

5 In a few minutes ....

6 The day after tomorrow ....

Pronunciation

/ɜ:/, /ɔ:/ and /əʊ/

> LOOK!
>
> Compare these sounds:
>
> c<u>ur</u>l   c<u>a</u>ll
> /ɜ:/   /ɔ:/
>
> b<u>ou</u>ght   b<u>oa</u>t
> /ɔ:/   /əʊ/
>
> g<u>ir</u>l   g<u>oa</u>l
> /ɜ:/   /əʊ/

8 **a)** 💾 Listen to the pairs of words in the chart and repeat them.

/ɜ:/	/ɔ:/	/əʊ/
turn	torn	
weren't		won't
shirt	short	
bird	bored	
learn		loan
work	walk	
	law	low
	caught	coat
burn		bone

b) 💾 Now listen and write the word you hear.

1 *loan* ....

2 ....

3 ....

4 ....

5 ....

6 ....

7 ....

8 ....

9 ....

10 ....

Vocabulary

Jobs

9 **a)** The pictures below show different jobs. Rearrange the mixed-up letters to make the name of each job.

1 ocnacntuat a.*ccountant*...........

2 realwy l..............................

3 nirdeegs d.............................

4 rarteyces s............................

5 enegrine e.............................

6 pitersnotice r...........................

7 retrucle l..............................

8 hicretcat a.............................

LOOK!

You can use your English–English dictionary to help you with word stress. The dictionary shows stress with this mark ' in front of the stressed syllable:

teach·er /'tiːtʃə/ n [C] someone whose job is to teach: *Miss Tindale's my favourite teacher*

re·port·er /rɪ'pɔːtə/ n [C] someone who writes about events for a newspaper, radio, or television

pol·i·ti·cian /pɒlɪ'tɪʃən/ n [C] someone who works in politics, especially an elected member of a parliament or similar institution

It's a good idea to mark the stress when you learn a new word. You can do this with a circle over the stressed syllable:

●　　　　●　　　●
teacher　politician　reporter

---

b) Using these extracts from the *Longman Dictionary of Contemporary English*, mark the stress ● on the jobs in a).

ac·coun·tant /ə'kaʊntənt/ n [C] someone whose job is to keep and check financial accounts

law·yer /'lɔːjə/ n [C] someone whose job is to advise people about laws, write formal agreements, or represent people in court

de·sign·er¹ /dɪ'zaɪnə/ n [C] someone whose job is to make plans or patterns for clothes, furniture, equipment etc: *a dress designer*

ar·chi·tect /'ɑːkɪtekt/ n [C] someone whose job is to design buildings

se·re·ta·ry /'sekrətəri/ n [C] someone who works in an office typing letters, keeping records, arranging meetings etc:

en·gi·neer¹ /endʒɪ'nɪə/ n [C] someone who designs the way roads, bridges, machines etc., are built

re·cep·tion·ist /rɪ'sepʃənɪst/ n [C] someone whose job is to welcome and deal with people arriving in a hotel or office building, visiting a doctor etc:

lecturer /'lektʃərə/ n [C] someone who gives a lecture: *a brilliant lecturer*

c) 🔊 Listen and repeat the words, paying attention to the stress.

Adjectives to describe jobs

10 **a)** Match an adjective from column A with a definition from column B.

	A		B
1	tiring	a	making you feel very sad
2	stressful	b	making you feel happy and satisfied because you feel you are doing something useful or important
3	challenging	c	making you feel that you want to sleep or rest
4	varied	d	producing or using new or imaginative ideas, results, etc.
5	creative	e	involving different kinds of things or people
6	depressing	f	makes you worry a lot
7	rewarding	g	difficult in an interesting or enjoyable way

1 ..c...　2 ....　3 ....　4 ....

5 ....　6 ....　7 ....

b) The adjectives are written in phonemic script below. Notice where the stressed syllable is. Complete each gap with the correct adjective, marking the stress ●.

1 *depressing*....... 5 ....
   /dɪˈpresɪŋ/   /ˈtaɪərɪŋ/

2 .... 6 ....
   /ˈstresfʊl/   /rɪˈwɔːdɪŋ/

3 .... 7 ....
   /krɪˈjeɪtɪv/   /ˈveərɪd/

4 ....
   /ˈtʃæləndʒɪŋ/

Real life
Formal telephone conversations

11 **a)** You are phoning Mrs Leeson, at Henderson Insurance. If you can't speak to her personally, you need her to phone you back. Complete the dialogue with suitable questions and responses.

A: Good afternoon, Henderson Insurance, Pam speaking. How can I help?

B: Good afternoon, could *I speak to Mrs Leeson please* .... ?

A: Just a moment, I'll put you through.

C: Hello, Mrs Leeson's office, Sandy speaking.

B: Hello, could ....
   .... ?

C: I'll just see if she's available. Can I ask who's calling?

B: ....

C: One moment please (*pause*). Hello, I'm afraid she's not in the office at the moment. Would you like her to call you back?

B: ....

C: Can I take your number?

B: ....

C: Right, I'll get her to call you back as soon as she comes in.

B: ....

C: Goodbye.

b) You are phoning International School to find out information about their English courses for executives. Leave a message on the ansaphone.

```
Ansaphone message:  This is the International School
answering service. We're sorry there's no one available
to take your call. Please leave your message after the
tone. If you would like information about courses,
please leave your name and address and we'll send you
our brochure. Thank you. (tone)
```

....
....
....

c) 🔲 Listen to some possible answers for a) and b)).

d) 🔲 Now try to respond in the spaces on the cassette, without looking at your book.

You hear:

Good afternoon, Henderson Insurance, Pam speaking. How can I help?

You say:

Good afternoon, could I speak to Mrs Leeson please?

Improve your writing
Apostrophes

> LOOK!
>
> We use apostrophes:
> • to show a missing letter or letters: *I am – I'm, He has – He's*.
> • to show possession with nouns: *Robin's pen*.
>
> Notice:
> • *the girl's mother* = one girl.
>   *the girls' mother* = more than one girl.
> • With irregular plurals, the apostrophe goes before the -s: *the children's game*.
> • We don't use apostrophes with possessive pronouns and adjectives: *hers, its, ours, theirs*.

12 Insert an apostrophe where necessary in these sentences.

a I read your pen friends letter – she sounds really nice.

b This is the boys bedroom. Theyre both at school at the moment.

c Its a nice day, isnt it?

d Whose is this? I think its hers.

e Whos that in reception?

f The companys lost all its best designers.

g Hes leaving in a years time.

h Ive got five years experience in advertising.

module 6

-ed / -ing adjectives

1 a) Complete the gaps in these sentences with an adjective from the box.

depressed / depressing   frightened / frightening
embarrassed / embarrassing   excited / exciting
disappointed / disappointing   annoyed / annoying
surprised / surprising

1 Rob's starting his new job tomorrow, isn't he?
   Yes, I think he's quite *excited* but very nervous too.

2 We were very .... to hear that Ann and Tom are going to get married. We didn't think that she liked him.

3 What did you think of the film?
   Actually, I thought it was quite .... I expected it to be better.

4 I was really .... because I couldn't remember his name and it was the third time I'd met him.

5 Some parents thought the film *Jurassic Park* was too .... for children under five years old.

6 Sally gets very .... when people are late for meetings.

7 Mrs Dudley's really .... Her cat died last week.

b) Complete the following sentences so that they are true for you.

1 I find .... terrifying.

2 I get very annoyed when ....
   ....

3 I'm always pleased when ....
   ....

4 When I get excited I usually ....

5 I find .... really boring.

6 I don't find .... shocking.

7 When I feel depressed I usually ....

Grammar snack

Prepositions after -ed / -ing adjectives

> LOOK!
>
> Adjectives can be followed by prepositions. A good dictionary shows you these: *depressed about*
>
> **de·pressed** /dɪ'prest/ *adj* a) feeling very unhappy: *She felt lonely and depressed.*| **[+ about]** *Carter seemed depressed about the situation*

2 a) Use these extracts from the *Longman Dictionary of Contemporary English* to find the prepositions which follow the adjectives below.

bored /bɔːd/ *adj* tired and impatient because you do not think something is interesting, or because you have nothing to do: *Children easily get bored.*| **[+ with]** *I'm bored with the same old routine day after day*

con·fused /kən'fjuːzd/ *adj* unable to understand clearly what someone is saying or what is happening: *I am totally confused. Could you explain that again?*| **[+ about]** *If you are confused about anything, phone my office*

dis·ap·point·ed /dɪsə'pɔɪntɪd/ *adj* sad because something you hoped for did not happen, or because someone or something was not as good as expected: *Dad seemed more disappointed than angry.*| **[+ about]** *Nathan's really disappointed about not being able to go*

fright·ened /'fraɪtnd/ *adj* feeling afraid: *a frightened animal*| **[+ of]** *I was frightened of being left by myself in the house*

in·terest·ed /'ɪntrestɪd/ *adj* giving a lot of attention to something because you want to find out more about it: **[+ in]** *I'm not really interested in politics*

sur·prised /sə'praɪzd/ *adj* having a feeling of surprise: *Mr Benson looked surprised when I told him I was leaving*| **[+ at/by]** *We were all surprised at Sue's outburst*

wor·ried /'wʌrid/ *adj* unhappy because you keep thinking about a problem or are anxious about something: *Don't look so worried – we'll find him.*| **[about]** *She's so worried about her exams*

em·bar·rassed /ɪm'bærəst/ *adj* ashamed, nervous, or uncomfortable in a social situation: *I managed to spill water on one of the guests – I was so embarrassed!*| **[+ about]** *At about the age of twelve, girls start feeling embarrassed about changing their clothes in front of other people*

1 bored *with*
2 confused ....
3 disappointed ....
4 frightened ....
5 interested ....
6 surprised ....
7 worried ....
8 embarrassed ....

b) Rewrite these sentences using the correct preposition.

1 The economy is depressing.

I'm *depressed about the economy* .

2 Stella found his behaviour surprising.

Stella was ....

3 Adrian's job interview is worrying him.

Adrian's ....

4 Missing the party was really disappointing.

I was ....

5 Your suggestions for the project are very interesting.

We're very ....

6 Henry's job is really boring.

Henry is ....

7 Roy found his big nose embarrassing.

Roy was ....

8 My daughter finds the dark frightening.

My daughter's ....

9 The reason for the meeting is confusing.

I'm ....

The passive

3 Look at the following sentences and write questions using the passive form.

a George was taken to hospital because he had a heart attack.   (ask *why*)

Why was George taken to hospital ?

b The prisoner was shot at 7 o'clock this morning. (ask *when*)

.... ?

c Tickets for the concert are sold at all large music stores.   (ask *where*)

.... ?

d The new theatre will be built in five years' time. (ask *when*)

.... ?

e The article was written by Urma Mackintyre. (ask *who by*)

.... ?

f The plant has been moved because it wasn't getting enough light.   (ask *why*)

.... ?

g Portuguese is spoken in Brazil.   (ask *where*)

.... ?

h Napoleon was known as Boney.   (ask *what*)

.... ?

i The film was directed by Zeffirelli.   (ask *who by*)

.... ?

j Forty-seven people have been injured.   (ask *how many*)

.... ?

4 Complete the gaps in these sentences with the correct passive form of the verb in brackets.

a In the UK psychology .... *is taught* .... in universities but not usually in schools.   (*teach*)

b The body of a young man .... in the river yesterday.   (*find*)

c Thirty-five cars .... from the city centre since January.   (*steal*)

d Where .... the next Olympics .... ?   (*hold*)

e Alcoholic drinks .... to children under 16.   (*not sell*)

f .... the bridge .... a long time ago?   (*build*)

g I'm sorry, but dinner .... in the price of an overnight stay.   (*not include*)

h .... the vegetables .... immediately after you pick them?   (*freeze*)

i The hole in my roof .... next Friday.   (*repair*)

j Mary .... about the accident yet.   (*not tell*)

5 Read these texts and complete the gaps with the best form (active or passive) of the verbs in bold below each text.

A

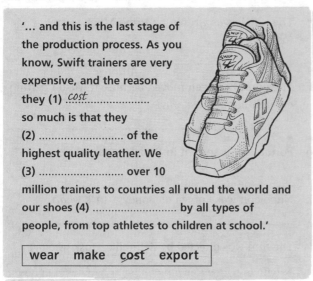

'... and this is the last stage of the production process. As you know, Swift trainers are very expensive, and the reason they (1) _cost_ so much is that they (2) .... of the highest quality leather. We (3) .... over 10 million trainers to countries all round the world and our shoes (4) .... by all types of people, from top athletes to children at school.'

| wear | make | cost | export |

B

'... and that (1) .... a track from the latest CD by Didi Brown. The songs (2) .... by Didi herself when she (3) .... in Ireland last year. The CD goes on sale next week and half the money from the sales (4) .... to the "Children In Need" fund.'

| write | give | stay | be |

C

This is the new Primera Consul Sir. As you can see it (1) .... The engine is much more powerful now and it (2) .... much quieter. There's a sun-roof which (3) .... when you press this button, and all models now (4) .... with a stereo radio/CD player included.'

| make | come | redesign | open |

Vocabulary

Films, TV and newspapers

6 a) Look at the clues below and find the words in the word square.

D	O	C	U	M	E	N	T	A	R	Y	Z
A	S	H	P	W	N	E	H	X	Y	I	L
N	W	A	R	Q	C	A	R	T	O	O	N
C	B	T	U	M	U	E	I	O	E	H	X
K	I	S	H	E	A	D	L	I	N	E	S
P	E	H	R	T	Y	N	L	A	Q	F	C
H	S	O	A	P	O	P	E	R	A	T	I
M	I	W	E	R	D	Q	R	M	R	A	E
M	U	S	I	C	A	L	P	L	T	R	N
V	A	L	W	I	N	G	R	X	I	L	C
G	I	L	S	A	H	A	I	T	C	M	E
A	D	V	E	R	T	M	P	E	L	S	S
S	E	W	E	L	R	E	V	I	E	W	O

1 A serious TV programme about real topics.
   A d_ocumentary_

2 A film about countries fighting.   A w _ _ film

3 A film where the characters are not real. They are drawn.   A c _ _ _ _ _ _

4 A piece of writing in a newspaper or a magazine.
   An a _ _ _ _ _ _

5 A TV programme which is on two or three times a week with a continuing story about people's lives.
   A s _ _ _ o _ _ _ _

6 A type of film with lots of singing and dancing.
   A m _ _ _ _ _ _

7 Titles of newspaper stories which are printed in large letters at the top of the stories.   h _ _ _ _ _ _ _

8 A short word for _advertisement_. An a _ _ _ _ _

9 A TV programme where famous people are interviewed about their lives and interests.   A c _ _ _ s _ _ _

10 A very exciting film about dangerous, frightening or mysterious events.   A t _ _ _ _ _ _ _

11 You can win prizes in this type of TV programme.
    A g _ _ _ show.

12 A film about events that take place in the future or in space.   A s _ _ _ _ _ _ -fiction film.

13 An article giving an opinion about a new film, play, book or exhibition.   A r _ _ _ _ _ _

b) 🔊 Listen to the words and repeat them.

Grammar snack

Prepositions for talking about books, films, etc.

> **LOOK!**
>
> We use these prepositions for talking about books:
> - *in* a book
> - *on* page 10
> - *in* the first chapter
> - *at* the beginning / end
> - *on* the front / back cover
>
> When we want to talk about where something takes place we say:
>
> - *Where's it on?* | It's
>   The film's | *on at the* + place
>   The concert's |
>
> It's *on at the* ABC cinema.

7 **a)** Complete the gaps in the chart below with the correct preposition.

Newspapers	Films	TV / Radio
in a newspaper	...... a film	...... TV / the radio
...... the sports section	...... the first / last scene	...... CNN / Radio Brussels
...... page 2	...... the beginning / end	...... a programme
...... the front / back page		...... the news
...... an advertisement		

b) Use the prompts to make complete answers to these questions.

1   Is there a photograph of the writer?   Yes / it / be / back cover.
Yes, it's on the back cover .

2   What happened to the hero in the play?   He / kill / last scene.
....

3   Where are the answers to these exercises?   They / be / page 65.
....

4   What's on TV tonight?   There / be / good film / Channel 4 at 8.30.
....

5   Where is the Picasso Exhibition on?   It / be / the National Gallery.
....

6   Where did you hear about the train accident?   radio / last night.
....

7   I can't find the TV guide in this newspaper.   It / be / back page.
....

8   Where are the film reviews?   I think they / be / entertainments section.
....

9   Was John on TV last night?   Yes, didn't you see him? He / be / *Break or Bust*.
....

Pronunciation

/f/, /v/ and /w/

> **LOOK!**
>
> Compare these three sounds:
>
> /f/: *fast, phrase*
> /v/: *very, leave*
> /w/: *where, flower*

8 **a)** 🔲 Listen to these sentences and mark the /f/, /v/ and /w/ sounds.

1   I was <u>f</u>ascinated by the
       /f/
     inter<u>v</u>ie<u>w</u> on T<u>V</u> last night.
       /v/ /w/   /v/

2   Ken goes swimming every week.

3   Phone me if you're confused about anything.

4   I'm terrified of storms, especially when I'm outside.

5   The weather forecast says it's going to get worse.

6   Philip drove over 1000 miles last week.

7   Don't forget to switch off the photocopier before you leave the office.

8   Do you believe in love at first sight?

9   That film got one of the worst reviews I've ever read.

10 I've just finished my homework. Can I go out?

b) Listen again and repeat the sentences.

Listen and read

Letters to a TV magazine

9 **a)** 📼 Read and / or listen to these letters. Which of the letters are positive and which are negative?

Ⓐ

Well done ABC for the brilliant series City Mysteries. The characters were really convincing and the stories completely believable. I was so disappointed when it finished. When will the next series be made? Are there any plans to release it on video?

G. Brown
Newtown

Ⓒ

Dear Editor,
I was really upset when I heard that the cartoon hour won't be shown on Saturday mornings any more. My brother and I used to watch it every week, especially *Superteenagers*, and we definitely don't like the boring gardening programme you've put on instead. Please, please, please give us back our cartoons!

David (aged 12)
Stonebridge

Ⓓ

This was the scene in my living room last Saturday: my two daughters were excited about staying up late that night to see Popswap their favourite programme, and I was looking forward to a calm half hour. Imagine how disappointed we all were when we heard that our programme had been replaced by Football Crazy. I understand that there was a very important match that night, but I do not understand why it needed a half hour introductory discussion!

Julie Grey
Cardiff

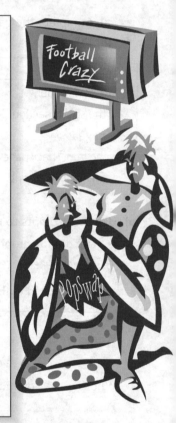

Ⓑ

I would like to congratulate Channel 6 for its marvellous documentary about the life and work of Louis Armstrong. His wonderful voice was loved by millions of people and he was a truly international entertainer. His death was a loss to all of us but his songs will live for ever.

S. Gascoigne
Queensborough

b) Mark these statements *T* (true) or *F* (false).

1   The series *City Mysteries* wasn't as good as G. Brown expected it to be. ..*F*..

2   G. Brown would like to have a copy of *City Mysteries*. .....

3   Louis Armstrong entertained people all over the world. .....

4   S. Gascoigne thought the acting in the Louis Armstrong programme was really good. .....

5   There's a new gardening programme on TV on Saturday mornings. .....

6   *Superteenagers* are real people. .....

7   *Popswap* was on at an earlier time than usual. .....

8   Julie Grey was interested in the football discussion. .....

1   Letter A: *positive* ....
2   Letter B: ....
3   Letter C: ....
4   Letter D: ....

Improve your writing

Linking ideas without repeating yourself

> **LOOK!**
>
> To avoid repeating words and expressions which have been used before, we often use:
> - possessive adjectives (*his, its, their*, etc.)
> - pronouns (*it, she, we*, etc.).
> - different vocabulary, e.g.
>
> Simon Strange's new novel is a murder mystery. The book is his sixth and it will go on sale next week.

10 **a)** What do the circled words refer back to in this letter? Draw arrows (⟵◯).

6 Beech Avenue,
Doncaster,
DO3 9BS.

15th April 199–

Dear Sir/Madam

I was really pleased to see that you're repeating the Girlz'n Boyz show on MTV. It's the best music programme around and has probably the most interesting guests on it.

I was really looking forward to last Friday's interview with the Saffron Girls but was very disappointed that you only showed three minutes of it. Why did you decide to cut the rest of the conversation, particularly the part where they were talking about their American tour? Please could you show the whole interview in another show soon.

Yours faithfully,

Jenny Philips

b) Choose a word from the box to replace the underlined words in the letter below.

| his | it | It | little boy | they | ~~its~~ | programme | it |

The cottage,
Castleton,
Derbyshire.

28th May, 199-

Dear Sir/Madam

I'd like to start by congratulating NBC on NBC's (1) _its_ new soap opera 'Buddies'. This soap opera (2) .... is very realistic and the soap opera (3) .... has become my family's favourite TV soap opera (4) ....

I'm rather confused, however, about NBC's rules on not showing violence before 8.00 at night. I was sitting with my 8-year-old son and my 8-year-old son's (5) .... friend, enjoying the story, but was extremely shocked by the murder scene, and my 8-year-old son (6) .... was very frightened by the murder scene (7) ....

Have the regulations changed? If the regulations (8) .... have, I think parents should know.

Yours faithfully,

Martin Cook

module 7

Polite requests

1 a) Find the mistake in each of these dialogues and correct it.

1 A: Is *it* ∧ alright if I close the window?
  B: Yes, go ahead.

2 A: Do you think could you turn your music down?
  B: Yes, of course. Sorry.

3 A: Would you helping me with my suitcase?
  B: I'm sorry, but I've got a bad back.

4 A: Could I pass the salt please?
  B: Yes, here you are.

5 A: Can I speak to you for a minute?
  B: Yes, I'm afraid so.

6 A: Will you to get me my glasses please?
  B: Sure.

7 A: Do you mind I go now?
  B: No, that's fine. We've nearly finished.

8 A: Would you mind taking these books to the library?
  B: Yes, I would. I'm going there anyway.

9 A: Could you possible hold my umbrella for a minute?
  B: Of course.

10 A: Would you mind look after Jane for an hour?
  B: I'm afraid I can't. I'm just going out.

b) 🖭 Listen to the dialogues and repeat them. Pay attention to the polite intonation.

2 a) Look at the following situations and complete each question so that it is polite.

1 You want to pay by credit card.
  Can *I pay by credit card* .... ?

2 You want to borrow your friend's camera.
  Do you think .... ?

3 You didn't hear what your classmate said. You want her to say it again.
  Could .... ?

4 You've written a letter in English. You want your teacher to check it.
  Would you mind .... ?

5 You can't hear what your flatmate is saying because of the radio. You want him to turn it down.
  Would .... ?

6 You need five pounds. You want your colleague to lend it to you.
  Do you think .... ?

7 You haven't finished your essay. You want to give it to your teacher a day late.
  Do you mind if .... ?

8 You need to use your colleague's computer.
  Could I possibly .... ?

9 Your friend asks you to go to the cinema with her. You can't tell her until tomorrow.
  Is it okay .... ?

b) 🖭 Listen to the situations and complete each question politely.

You hear:

> You want to pay by credit card.
> Can ...

You say:

> Can I pay by credit card?

Ways of making offers

> **LOOK!**
>
> Here are some different ways of making offers:
>
> • I'll **carry** that (for you) (if you like).
>
> • Shall I **carry** that (for you)?
>
> • Would you like me **to** carry that (for you)?
>
> • Do you want me **to** carry that (for you)?

3 Look at these dialogues and reorder B's response to make an offer. The first word is underlined.

a A: Oh no! I've forgotten to phone Jon about the football match!

   B: phone – like – if – him – <u>I'll</u> – you

   I'll phone him if you like .

b A: I'd really love a drink.

   B: for – you – <u>Shall</u> – get – I – beer – a ?

   .... ?

c A: I can't get this video to work.

   B: me – want – you – try – <u>Do</u> – to ?

   .... ?

d A: Oh no, I'm going to miss my train.

   B: like – station – me – take – <u>Would</u> – to – you – to – you – the ?

   ....

   .... ?

e A: I really like that tape.

   B: to – like – <u>I'll</u> – if – lend – you – it – you

   ....

   ....

f A: That's a very interesting article.

   B: you – copy – want – a – <u>Do</u> – make – you – me – to ?

   ....

   .... ?

g A: Can you give me some information about your holidays in Greece?

   B: you – our – send – to – brochure – <u>Would</u> – me – like – you ?

   ....

   .... ?

h A: Have you got the address of that electrician?

   B: down – <u>Yes</u> – I – it – for – shall – write – you ?

   ....

   .... ?

will (instant decisions and responses)

4 **a)** Choose a sentence from each box to make a dialogue for the situations below.

A

> The black ones look really nice, Madam. Are they comfortable?
>
> How much longer are you going to be in the bathroom?
>
> Could you possibly change my flight to the evening?
>
> Is there anything good on TV tonight?
>
> Hi! Nice to see you. Come in and have a coffee.
>
> Are you ready to order?
>
> Could I speak to Mrs Williams in the Accounts Department?
>
> I've got a problem with my shower. It isn't working.

B

> Yes, very – I'll take them.
>
> Okay, but I won't stay long, I can see you're busy.
>
> Yes, I'll have the fish.
>
> I'll just check the computer.
>
> I don't know – I'll have a look in the newspaper.
>
> I'll just see if she's available. Hold on please.
>
> I'll send someone up straightaway. Which room is it?
>
> Okay, okay, I won't be long.

1 In a shoe shop.
   A: *The black ones look really nice, madam. Are they comfortable?*
   B: ....

2 In a hotel.
   A: ....
      ....
   B: ....
      ....

3 In a travel agent's.
   A: ....
      ....
   B: ....

4 Visiting a friend's house.
   A: ....
      ....
   B: ....
      ....

5 In a restaurant.
   A: ....
   B: ....

6 Phoning someone's office.
   A: ....
      ....
   B: ....
      ....

7 At home in the evening, relaxing.
   A: ....
   B: ....
      ....

8 At home in the morning, getting ready for work.
   A: ....
      ....
   B: ....

b) 🔊 Listen to the first line of each dialogue and use the prompt to respond.

You hear: **You say:**

The black ones look really nice, Madam. Are they comfortable? (take / them)

Yes, very – I'll take them.

Jazz chant (go)

5 **a)** Complete the gaps in the jazz chant with one of the phrases from the box. Use the Present Simple in the first verse and the Past Simple in the second verse.

go swimming   go out   go to bed   go for
go away   go round   go out

On Mondays I always (1) *go out* for a drink

And have a good long chat.

On Tuesdays I often (2) .... a walk

Then (3) .... to my best friend's flat.

On Wednesdays and Thursdays I stay at home

And (4) .... at eight.

On Fridays I sometimes (5) .... for a meal

And get back really late!

I (6) .... for most weekends

To the beach and my house by the sea.

I (7) .... and shopping on Saturdays

And on Sundays I'm home by three.

On Monday John (8) *went out* for a drink

And had a good long chat.

On Tuesday night he (9) .... a walk

Then (10) .... to his best friend's flat.

On Wednesday and Thursday he stayed at home

And (11) .... at eight.

On Friday night he (12) .... for a meal

And got back really late.

He (13) .... for the whole weekend

To the beach and his house by the sea.

He (14) .... late on Saturday

And was dead by half past three!

b) 🔊 Listen to the jazz chant and try to say it with the cassette.

Grammar snack

Articles: making generalisations

LOOK!

When we are talking about people or things **in general**, we use a plural or an uncountable noun with **no** article:
• *I like films and music* (**all** films and music).
• *I like people with a sense of humour* (**all** people with a sense of humour).

Exception:
• *I hate **the** noise **of** computer games.*

For very **specific** people and things we use **the**:
• *I liked **the** films shown in the festival.*
• ***The** people next door have a noisy dog.*

6 Complete the gaps in these pairs of sentences with the correct word or phrase from the box.

exercise   the exercise   poetry   the poetry
traffic   the traffic   music   the music   people
the people   men / women   the men / the women

a 1 *Traffic* is one of the biggest problems in our cities.
  2 You're late! Yes, ... on the way here was really bad.

b 1 What a dreadful party! .... all talked about children and .... all talked about football!
  2 .... are physically stronger than ....

c 1 I was doing .... you showed me for 20 minutes yesterday and it really made my legs ache!
  2 .... is good for you.

d 1 My husband really hates .... who chew gum all the time.
  2 I thought .... at the next table were very rude to the waiter.

e 1 Grace doesn't like listening to .... when she works.
  2 .... they play on that radio station is dreadful!

f 1 .... of William Wordsworth is very emotional.
  2 We studied .... at school, but I haven't read much since.

47

Listen and read

Food from other countries

7 **a)** Sun, Maria and Maciej are talking about meals in their countries. Read and / or listen to the texts and complete the chart.

Sun (Korean)

'Well, my mum is Korean and she told me that for breakfast people often have rice with a kind of soup that has got seaweed in it, you know, the plant that grows in the sea. Then for lunch the children usually take a lunchbox with them to school with rice and kimchi in it. Kimchi's a kind of mixed vegetable dish. It's got hot pepper in it. It's very common in Korea and you can have it for any meal. Then dinner is the big meal of the day. People tend to have kimchi and rice again and soup. They might also have some meat, which they cook on a hot plate on the table in front of them while they're having the soup. The meat is often chicken or pork and you can put soya sauce in it.'

Maria (Italian)

'Well, for breakfast of course I have cappuccino, which is coffee with a lot of milk in it, and you make it in a special machine. You can put chocolate powder on it if you like. I usually have a cornetto with it, that's a kind of sweet bread in a crescent shape, like a French croissant. And for lunch, well I usually have a sandwich because I have my main meal in the evening. For that my favourite starter is minestrone soup which has lots of vegetables and small pasta shapes in it. Then I often have fish, or something simple like that which is easy to cook. And then, if I want a special treat, I might have tiramisu for dessert. It's very rich and quite complicated to make. It's got lots of cream in it with cake and cold coffee and liqueur. Then, of course, I have a strong espresso coffee to finish it off!'

Maciej (Polish)

'For breakfast I have a kind of open sandwich with ham and cheese or tomatoes in it. And then I often go out for lunch. A popular lunch is pierogi ruski, which are a bit like ravioli, except they've got potatoes with cheese and onion in them. And then in the evening ... well in Poland most people eat a bigger meal in the evening. For example, kotlet is a traditional dish, that's meat fried in egg and breadcrumbs, often pork. I also like bigos which is a kind of stew – sometimes you cook it for hours – it's got cabbage, well sauerkraut, and different kinds of meat in it – you know, ham, bacon, sausage ... you can put dried mushrooms in it too. You have it just with bread.'

	Sun	Maria	Maciej
Breakfast	*people often have rice …*		
Lunch			
Dinner			

> **LOOK!**
>
> • **It's got** pepper / seaweed / ham / cabbage / mushrooms / soya beans **in it**.
>
> • **You can put** soya sauce / dried mushrooms / chilli / chocolate / cheese / breadcrumbs **in / on it**.
>
> • **It's a kind of** stew / starter / dessert / cake / meat dish / sauce / pie etc.
>
> • **It's** easy / quick / complicated / difficult **to make / cook**.
>
> • **You can have it for** any meal / breakfast / a snack / dinner etc.
>
> • **It's a** traditional / light / rich / common / popular **dish**.
>
> • **It's a bit like / It tastes a bit like** ravioli / yogurt / pork etc.

b) In your notebook write about a typical dish in your country / region or something you tried when you were in another country. Show it to your teacher.

Vocabulary

Food and cooking

8 Circle the word which does not belong in each group.

a   cabbage   spinach   carrot   (peach)

b   plum   melon   cauliflower   pineapple

c   prawn   lamb   pork   beef

d   mayonnaise   garlic   soya sauce   ketchup

e   saucepan   spoon   mixing bowl   frying pan

f   boil   chop   roast   bake

g   tough   overdone   delicious   burnt

h   fork   corkscrew   tin opener   bottle opener

i   fresh   frozen   spicy   tinned

49

Pronunciation

Lost letters

9 a) In these words from module 7 one or more of the letters is not pronounced. Cross out the 'lost' letter/s. Say the word aloud to see what is missing and also use the phonemic script.

1 average
/ˈævrɪdʒ/

2 restaurant
/ˈrestrɒnt/

3 vegetable
/ˈvedʒtəbəl/

4 international
/ɪntəˈnæʃnəl/

5 considered
/kənˈsɪdəd/

6 different
/ˈdɪfrənt/

7 interestingly
/ˈɪntrəstɪŋli/

8 offering
/ˈɒfrɪŋ/

9 traditional
/trəˈdɪʃnəl/

10 served
/sɜːvd/

11 marriage
/ˈmærɪdʒ/

12 business
/ˈbɪznɪs/

b) 🖳 Listen and repeat the words. Pay attention to the stress.

Improve your writing

Sending and replying to invitations by e-mail

10 a) Read these e-mails and find three invitations and their replies.

(A) We're having a few people to stay for the weekend from 17-19 August and I was wondering if you'd like to come. We're hoping it'll be nice enough to have picnics, go swimming, etc. Let me know as soon as you can, hope you're well, regards

(B) That's great news. Of course I'd love to come to the wedding. You'll have to send me the wedding list. Or maybe I should just buy you a surprise present?!

(C) Hello there. I hope you're not too busy. Could you possibly come to a meeting tomorrow at 10.30, to discuss the new book? I'm sorry it's such short notice.

(D) Thanks very much for the invitation. I'm afraid I've arranged to go to my parents' wedding anniversary party that weekend, so I won't be able to come. What a shame – some other time, perhaps?

(E) Yes, I think I can make it. I'll have to leave before 12.00 though, because I've got to be on the other side of town for lunch. I hope that's alright and look forward to seeing you tomorrow.

(F) I know it's a strange time to be sending e-mail, but I can't sleep! Jon and I have decided to get married and I wanted you to be the first person I invited to the wedding. It's going to be in Dublin on Saturday September 9th. I'll send you a proper invitation in the post – but I do hope you can come. If you're still awake, please reply!

1 an invitation to a meeting ....C.., reply ....

2 a wedding invitation ...., reply ....

3 an invitation to stay for the weekend ...., reply ....

b) Look at the e-mails again and underline useful phrases for inviting and for accepting or refusing an invitation. Now write an invitation (using e-mail if you have it at home / work / school) and show it to your teacher.

module 8

Defining relative clauses

1 Pete is talking to Les about his holiday plans. Look at the relative pronouns in **bold** and bracket the ones which can be omitted.

PETE: We're thinking of going to Spain this year. You went there last year, didn't you?

LES: Yes, that's right. Actually I've got some photos *(which)* I can show you of where we went. It was Mohacar on the south coast. A friend **whose** daughter went there last year recommended it.

PETE: Oh, someone **who** I work with has been to Mohacar. It's a very quiet area, isn't it?

LES: Yes, the thing **that** I liked most about it was the relaxing atmosphere. It's a place **where** you can forget all your problems.

PETE: How do you get there?

LES: Well you can fly to Almeria, but that's quite expensive, or you can take any flight **which** goes to Malagar and drive east along the coast. I know several people **who** have done that. Anyway, do you want to see the photos?

2 a) Here are the photos from Les's holiday last year. Les is talking about the photos. Join his two sentences to make one, using a relative pronoun.

2

a This is the balcony. We had breakfast there every morning …

....

....

b … and this is the beach. It was right in front of our apartment.

....

....

1

a This is the apartment. We rented it …
   This is the apartment which / that we rented

b … and these are the people. They were staying in the apartment next door.

....

....

3

a This is a bar. It stayed open till three in the morning …

....

....

b … and this is the man. He owned it.

....

4

a This is a fish restaurant. We had excellent meals there ...

....

b ... and this is a woman. Her mother cooked wonderful paella.

....

5

a This is one day. We went on a boat trip ...

....

b ... and these are the men. We borrowed their boat.

....

6

a This is a market. It was open every Wednesday ...

....

b ... and this is me wearing a hat. I bought it there.

....

b) Look again at the sentences you have made and bracket the relative pronoun if it can be omitted.

Prepositions with defining relative clauses

LOOK!

- *She's the woman who I **spoke to**.*
- *I'd like a balcony that I could **sit on** when it's hot.*

When we use a verb or preposition in defining relative clauses, the preposition comes at the end of the clause.

3 Complete the gaps in the sentences below with a preposition from the box.

| on to in with |

a Do you have a knife which I could cut this string *with* ?

b Is there someone my son could talk .... about his exams?

c Have you got something we could open this bottle .... ?

d Angus needs a new diary he can write all his appointments ....

e Holly would like a radio which she could listen .... while she's in the bath.

f Our office needs a photocopier we can do coloured copies ....

g Have you got anything I could dry these dishes .... ?

h Is there someone we could discuss our problem .... ?

Quantifiers (*a few, a lot of*, etc.)

4 Sandra is trying to persuade Aileen to go with her to a party, but Aileen is very depressed and doesn't want to go. Match Aileen's comments with a response from Sandra.

Aileen:

a) I haven't got anything to wear.

b) I've got no friends.

c) I haven't got much money.

d) I don't like parties where there are too many people.

e) I never have enough to talk about.

f) I've got too much work to do.

g) There's no time to get ready.

Sandra:

1) You've got some time to finish it tomorrow.

2) There's plenty of time – we don't need to be there until 9.

3) Don't be stupid, you've got lots of interesting things to say.

4) Come on – you've got loads of friends.

5) But you've got some really nice clothes.

6) You only need enough for a taxi.

7) Oh, but not many people have been invited tonight.

a) .....5..... b) .... c) .... d) .... e) .... f) .... g) ....

5 a) There is one mistake in each of these sentences. Find the mistake and correct it.

1 Now my father is retired he's got plenty ~~of~~ time for his hobby, making model boats.

2 'Thank you all very much. You've given me a lot good ideas for the new school building. Now all we need is enough money to pay for it!'

3 There were too many of people and too much noise so Greg couldn't see or hear the President.

4 Lisbon's got loads of good shops but there's not much of parking space in the city centre.

5 There are plenty of tickets left for the afternoon performance but no many for the evening one.

6 I think there's too much pepper in the soup but not enough of salt.

7 'Can I have plenty fruit but not much cream please.'

b) Complete these sentences so that they are true for you.

1 I've got too many ....
....

2 There are a lot of ....
.... in my bedroom.

3 I haven't got enough ....
....

4 I don't drink much ....
....

5 I eat plenty of ....
....

6 I don't know any ....
....

7 I read loads of ....
....

8 I do a lot of ....
....

53

Grammar snack

Articles with countable / uncountable nouns

> LOOK!
> • 'You've got **a** very high temperature.'
> • '**The** temperature in this room is very cold.'
>
> With countable nouns we can use *a/an* or *the*.
>
> • 'What ø horrible weather!'
> • '**The** weather in England is changeable.'
>
> With uncountable nouns we cannot use *a/an* but we can use *the*.

6 a) Put the nouns in these extracts from the *Longman Dictionary of Contemporary English* into the correct column in the chart.

sce·ne·ry /ˈsiːnəri/ *n* [U] the natural features of a particular part of a country, such as mountains, forests, deserts etc: *The best part of the trip was the scenery. It was fantastic.*

view¹ /vjuː/ *n* [C] what you are able to see or the possibility of seeing it: **have a good/bad/wonderful etc view (of)** (= be able to see a lot, very little etc) *We had a really good view of the whole stage from where we were sitting.*|

guest-house /ˈɡesthaʊs/ *n* [C] a private house where people can pay to stay and have meals

ac·com·mo·da·tion /əkɒməˈdeɪʃən/ *n* [U] a place for someone to stay, live, or work in: *rented accommodation*

travel² *n* [U] the act or activity of travelling: *Snow has disrupted travel in many parts of the country.*

tem·pe·ra·ture /ˈtempərətʃə/ *n* [C] a measure of how hot or cold a place or thing is: *The temperature of the water was just right for swimming.*|a **temperature of 20°/100° etc.** *Water boils at a temperature of 100° C.*|

weath·er¹ /ˈweðə/ *n* [U] the temperature and other conditions such as rain, and wind: **the weather** *What was the weather like on your vacation?*|

mon·ey /ˈmʌni/ *n* [U] what you earn by working and what you spend in order to buy things: *The repairs will cost a lot of money.*

price¹ c/praɪs/ *n* [C] the amount of money for which something is sold, bought, or offered: *Fuel prices are rising steadily.* | [+ of] *Can you tell me what the price of a new window would be?*|

journey¹ /ˈdʒɜːni/ *n* [C] a trip from one place to another, especially over a long distance: *a train journey across Europe*|

Countable	Uncountable
view	

b) Complete the gaps in these sentences with *a/an*, *the* or nothing (–).

1 Hello, how nice to see you. Did you have ..*a*..... good journey?

2 Susan, could you book .... accommodation for a group of twenty coming to the Conference.

3 What .... beautiful view! You're very lucky to live here.

4 Have you got .... money I lent you?

5 Mr Schmidt had .... bad weather on the way here.

6 There are plenty of opportunities for .... travel in this job.

7 You need to keep this liquid at .... very low temperature.

8 There's .... amazing scenery all around the hotel.

9 .... price of a ticket to Majorca has gone down.

10 My colleague Tessa stayed in .... wonderful guest house in the South of France.

Vocabulary

Formation of nouns

7 a) Make the verbs in the box into nouns, using the ending *-ment*, *-sion* or *-tion*. Pay attention to the spelling.

> invent   equip   treat   compete   argue   permit
> operate   advertise   explain   produce   persuade
> decide   improve   revise   discuss

-ment	-sion	-tion
		invention

b) 🔲 Listen to the words and repeat them, paying attention to the stress.

c) Complete the gaps in these sentences with the correct noun or verb from Exercise a). You may need to change the form of the verb.

1 There's been an extraordinary _improvement_ in computer design over the last 20 years.

2 I saw an .... in the newspaper for a new type of vacuum cleaner that doesn't need a bag.

3 There's a lot of .... between mobile phone companies.

4 After a lot of discussion, Tom .... me to have a fax machine at home.

5 After the video broke down for the fifth time, Diane .... to buy a new one.

6 There's a shop in the main street which sells very good sports ....

Pronunciation

/ʒ/, /ʃ/, /dʒ/ and /tʃ/

> **LOOK!**
> Compare these sounds:
> _television_ **shop** _journey_ _teacher_
> /ʒ/   /ʃ/   /dʒ/   /tʃ/

8 a) 📼 Listen to these words (or say them aloud) and write the correct symbol underneath.

1 invention
   /ʃ/

2 research
   / /

3 decision
   / /

4 measure
   / /

5 permission
   / /

6 object
   / /

7 temperature
   / /

8 agency
   / /

9 production
   / /

10 persuasion
   / /

11 exchange
   / /

12 discussion
   / /

b) Listen again and repeat the words, paying attention to the stress.

Reading

9 Read this advert about cordless headphones and mark the statements below _T_ (true) or _F_ (false).

Want to listen to your favourite CD in the garden without disturbing the neighbours?

Try our incredible new cordless* radio frequency headphones.

These new headphones allow you to tune into your favourite radio station or TV programme in complete privacy. The sound quality is excellent, and the lightweight headset is so comfortable you won't notice you're wearing it. You don't even need to be in the same room as your Hi-fi or TV to enjoy your favourite sounds.

Just plug the special transmitter into your TV or stereo!

HEADPHONES

◆ The sound goes straight to your headphones and no one else will hear it!

◆ The sound signal is strong enough to go through walls, ceilings and doors!

◆ There's a volume control on the headset itself.

◆ Relax in your garden. Listen to your favourite CD without disturbing the neighbours.

These headphones are amazing value at £34.95 inc. postage with extra sets of headphones available for just £24.95 each.

Order yours today!
Place your order on our 24-hour credit hotline.
01044 232467 – 24-hour ordering service 7 days a week.

Please allow up to 7 days for delivery. If you are not fully satisfied, we will return your money if you return the goods undamaged within 7 days.
* _cordless_ means there is no wire. You can have cordless irons and kettles.

a The headset doesn't weigh very much. ..T..

b You need to take the transmitter to the place where you want to listen. .....

c You can't use these headphones to listen to something that's in a room downstairs from where you are. .....

d If you want to turn the music up you don't need to go back to the room where the CD or television is. .....

e You have to pay extra for the postage. .....

f A second set of headphones costs less than the first one. .....

g You can ring the credit hotline at any time of the day or night. .....

h You should receive your goods after 7 days. .....

Improve your writing

Formal and informal styles

10 **a)** Look at these two letters about things which have been lost. The first is informal and the second is more formal. Complete the gaps with the correct phrase from the box.

> I don't suppose you've found it / I do hope it has been found
>
> could you post it / I would be grateful if you could send it
>
> let me know how much the postage is / I will of course pay for postage
>
> I am writing to enquire whether / Just writing to say

---

46 Broom Way

Feb. 23rd

Dear Andy,

(1) *Just writing to say* ....
thanks again for having us last weekend. We both had a really good time.

The only thing is, I've lost one of my earrings: I know I was wearing it on Sunday and when we got home, I couldn't find it. Perhaps it fell off while I was playing with the children in the garden.

(2) .... ?

I don't know if you remember it. It's quite big, made of silver, with a blue stone set in it. The earrings are quite special to me because they were a birthday present from Peter.

If you do happen to find it,

(3) ....
to me? Obviously,

(4) ....

Anyway, I'll keep my fingers crossed!

Lots of love,
Ingrid.

---

22 Prince Avenue,
Horbury.

March 27th 199_

The Manager,
Sherbon Hotel,
Vermont.

Dear Sir/Madam,

(5) ....
you have found a camera which I left in my hotel room last weekend. I was staying in room 201 from 21st–23rd. I am almost certain that I left the camera in the bedside cabinet.

(6) ....
since it is a very expensive model. It is a Nikon compact, in a black leather case with a red and black strap.

(7) ....
by registered post to the above address.

(8) ....

Yours faithfully,

I. Crompton.

---

b) Imagine that you have just finished a language course in the UK, and you realise that you have left something in a classroom. Write to the school to ask about it. The address is: *Success* Language School, Dewbury Road, Brighton. Write the letter in your notebook and show it to your teacher.

module 9

Futures for prediction (*will, might, may,* etc.)

1 Reorder the words in these sentences. The first word is underlined.

a tonight – see – <u>I'll</u> – definitely – John
I'll definitely see John tonight .

b probably – pass – <u>Carlos</u> – exam – English – his – won't
....
....

c so – may – us – late – don't – <u>We</u> – for – wait – be
....
....

d get – isn't – to – <u>Chris</u> – job – likely – the
....

e next – almost – <u>I'll</u> – English – year – do – here – certainly – an – course
....
....

f stay – New York – decide – in – <u>Teresa</u> – might – to – well
....
....

g weekend – away – probably – <u>We'll</u> – this – go
....

h lots – are – on – <u>There</u> – the – likely – beach – be – to – people – of
....
....

2 a) Rewrite these sentences so that they mean the same, using the words in brackets.

1 Brazil are likely to win the World Cup.
Brazil <u>may well win the World Cup</u> . (*may well*)

2 I don't think we'll have time to do any sightseeing.
We ....
.... (*definitely*)

3 It'll probably rain before the end of the day.
It ....
.... (*likely*)

4 Perhaps my friend Mari will be a famous actress one day.
My friend Mari ....
.... (*could*)

5 My boss is very unlikely to agree to the pay rise.
My boss ....
.... (*almost certainly*)

6 I think you'll recognise my sister when you see her.
You ....
.... (*probably*)

7 We probably won't get back from the theatre before midnight.
We ....
.... (*likely*)

8 I'm sure that our teacher will give us a lot of homework for the weekend.
Our teacher ....
.... (*almost certainly*)

b) 🖭 Listen to the sentences and change them, using the prompts given.

You hear:

> Brazil are likely to win the World Cup. (may well)

You say:

> *Brazil may well win the World Cup.*

Hypothetical possibilities with *if*

3

a) Match a question from column A with an answer from column B.

A

1　If you won a lot of money, would you spend it all straightaway?

2　What would you do if someone tried to rob you in the street?

3　If your car broke down on the motorway, what would you do?

4　Would you know what to do if someone cut their arm badly?

5　If you knew a friend of yours was stealing money from his company, would you tell anyone?

6　Would you feel safe walking home alone at night in your town?

7　If someone offered you a free bungee jump, what would you do?

8　Could you ever eat raw meat?

B

a　I'd probably just give him all my money and run!

b　No, I definitely wouldn't – it's too dangerous.

c　I think I'd probably tie something round it.

d　I might do it if I was feeling brave!

e　I'd go and look for a telephone.

f　I might tell another friend, so that we could decide what to do.

g　If I was hungry enough, yes!

h　No, I'd invest some of it.

1 ..*h*.　2 ....　3 ....　4 ....　5 ....　6 ....

7 ....　8 ....

b) What would *you* do in the situations above? Write your answers below using *I'd, I wouldn't, I might, I could*.

1　...

2　...

3　...

4　...

5　...

6　...

7　...

8　...

Real and hypothetical possibilities

4

Complete the gaps in these conversations with the best form of the verb in brackets.

a) Clare's going to have a baby. She's talking to her friend Jackie about it.

CLARE:　I can't decide whether to have the baby in hospital or not.

JACKIE:　Well, I (1) *'d go* .... (*go*) into hospital, especially as it's your first baby.

CLARE:　Yes, you're probably right.

JACKIE:　Have you decided on a name yet?

CLARE:　Yes – if it (2) .... (*be*) a boy, we (3) .... (*call*) him Tom, and if it (4) .... (*be*) a girl, Sara.

b) Tim's mother is very worried because she's had a letter from his school, saying that he has missed a lot of lessons.

MOTHER:　Why aren't you going to your classes?

TIM:　Because they're so boring: I (1) .... (*go*) if they (2) .... (*be*) more interesting. And I always get bad marks.

MOTHER:　Well, that's not surprising: if you (3) .... (*spend*) less time playing computer games and (4) .... (*work*) harder, you (5) .... (*not / have*) so many problems.

If sentences in social situations

LOOK!

We often use *if* sentences in the following ways:

- Asking for permission:
  Would you mind if I **opened** the window?
  Would you mind if I **left** early today?

- Giving advice:
  If I **were** you, **I'd** go home.
  You'll feel much better if you **have** a rest.

- Making offers:
  I'll phone her if you **like**.
  I'll fetch your car if you **give** me the keys.

- Accepting invitations:
  'Thank you, that **would** be very nice.'

5 a) Use the prompts to write complete sentences in these situations.

1 Your friend has a letter to post. You are going out and offer to post it.
post it / if / want
I'll post it if you want .

2 It's your first evening with a host family in England and you want to telephone home. How do you ask your landlady?
alright / if / I / use / phone?
.... ?

3 Your friend is expecting a call from John, but she has to go out. What do you say?
I / take / message / if / he / phone
....

4 You're on a crowded train and you want to open the window. How do you ask the other passengers?
anyone mind / if / I / open a window?
....

5 Your car's broken down and a friend offers to take you home. What does he say?
I / give / you / lift / if / like
....

6 A friend invites you to eat in a new restaurant. What do you say?
That / be / great!
....

7 It's snowing heavily and your friend wants to drive home. How do you advise her?
I / not / drive in this weather / if / I / be / you
....

b) 🔊 Listen to the situations and respond, using the prompts.

You hear:

Your friend has a letter to post. You are going out and you offer to post it. I'll ...

You say:

I'll post it if you want.

Grammar snack

Word order of adverbs (*certainly, probably, definitely*)

LOOK!

The adverb comes before the **main** verb in a positive sentence:
- *I **definitely** told her.*
- *She's **probably** working too hard.*
- *I'll **almost certainly** see you next week.*

Notice: When *to be* is a main verb (not an auxiliary) the adverb comes after it:
- *I was **definitely** at home at 10.30.*

The adverb comes before the **auxiliary** verb in a negative sentence:
- *I **definitely** didn't tell her.*
- *She **probably** isn't working hard enough.*
- *I **almost certainly** won't see you next week.*

6 Rewrite these sentences, putting the adverb in brackets into the correct position.

a The waitress has made a mistake with the bill. (*definitely*)
The waitress has definitely made a mistake with the bill

b My aunt won't hear the phone. (*almost certainly*)
....

c Don't ask Nick about the lecture: he wasn't listening. (*probably*)
....

d It's 11.00: they've missed their train. (*almost certainly*)
....

e Stephen doesn't smoke. (*definitely*)
....

f Don't ring Kate, she isn't home yet. (*probably*)
....

g Jos didn't take the money: he was with me all day. (*definitely*)
....

Vocabulary

Money verbs and prepositions

7 **a)** Read these paragraphs about what people do with money, and circle the correct preposition.

Ⓐ

'I don't know why my daughter wastes money (1) by / on unnecessary things like magazines and make up. If she was more careful and put a little money (2) into / for the bank every month, she could save up (3) for / on something really nice, like a new CD player.'

Ⓑ

'I'm really fed up with my boyfriend: he never has any money. He doesn't pay (4) on / for drinks or a meal when we go out, and you can see that he never spends any money (5) in / on clothes! In fact, I don't think I've ever seen him take any money (6) off / out of the bank.'

Ⓒ

'My grandma is really old-fashioned: she hates banks. When she goes shopping she always pays (7) on / in cash: she thinks that if you pay (8) with / by cheque or credit card, it's not 'real' money. She's got lots of money, though, and I'm always telling her to invest it (9) in / into some kind of business, instead of keeping it under the mattress.'

b) Complete the gaps in these sentences with the best form of a verb from the box and / or the correct preposition.

waste	invest	put	take	pay (x 3)
save up	spend			

1 Bob: Each month I ..put......... about a quarter of my salary ..into... the bank, because I'm .... a holiday in the Bahamas and I'm really trying not to .... money .... stupid things like beer and lottery tickets.

2 Sheila: I don't carry much cash around with me. When I go shopping for food, I usually .... cheque.

3 Katie: My mum .... all my clothes, and she gives me some money every week to .... sweets and magazines.

4 Paul: I don't like .... money .... a cash dispenser when it's late at night. I know someone who was robbed while he was doing that.

5 Jack: I do a lot of small building jobs for people, so I prefer it if they .... me .... cash. I suppose about three quarters of my customers do this.

6 Maria: Well, my souvenir shop's doing very well at the moment, so I'm planning to .... two thirds of the profits .... another shop.

Improve your writing

Opening a bank account

If you go to stay in an English-speaking country for more than a few months you may want to open a bank account.

Application to open a current account

PLEASE COMPLETE IN BLOCK CAPITALS

Title: ....   Surname: ....

First name(s): ....

Date of birth: ....

Nationality: ....

Address: ....

....

....

Postcode ....

Tel: Home No. ....   Work No. ....

Marital status: ....   Number of dependent children: ....

Where do you live?   With parents ❑   Alone ❑

With partner ❑   Other ❑

Previous address: ....

....

....

Postcode ....

When did you move to your current address?

Month ....   Year ....

What type of other bank or building society accounts do you hold?

Current ❑   Savings/Deposit ❑   Other ❑

How many of each of the following payment cards do you have?

Credit card ❑   Store cards ❑   Debit cards ❑

Employment status (e.g. full-time / part-time / student): ....

Job title (e.g. Sales assistant): ....

Employer's name and address / Place of study: ....

....

....

Postcode ....

When did you start working for your current employer / start your course of studies?   Month ....   Year ....

Mother's maiden name: ....

(This personal information may be required as identification for security measures only.)

Signature ....

Date ....

---

8 **a)** Look at the vocabulary from the form and match each word or phrase (1–9) with a definition / example (a–i).

1 title
2 marital status
3 mother's maiden name
4 current account
5 deposit account
6 postcode
7 store card
8 credit card
9 debit card

a single – married – divorced
b You can use this card to buy something and pay at the end of the month.
c You use this account for saving.
d Your mother's surname before she was married.
e Mrs – Mr – Ms – Miss
f You can use this card to buy things at a particular shop, e.g. a department store.
g You can take money from this account whenever you like.
h You can use this card in the same way as a cheque. The money is taken directly from your bank account.
i SE4 2NP (this shows the area that you live in).

1 ...*e*...   2 ....   3 ....   4 ....   5 ....   6 ....   7 ....

8 ....   9 ....

b) You have come to the UK for a year. Decide whether you have come to:

- work for FBT Inc. as a trainee manager. The company's office is at: 7 Grosvenor Place, London WC1 2RP.

- take an English course. The address of the school is: *International English*, 40 Baker Street, London NW1.
  You have rented a flat at this address: Flat 3, 2 Croxted Road, London SE14 2PQ. Phone number: 0181 629 4731. Now complete the bank application form and ask your teacher to check it.

Listen and read

Lottery winners

9 a) Which of these things do you expect people to do if they win a lottery 'jackpot' (the biggest prize)?

1 give up their job / stay in the same job?
2 stay in their old house / buy a new house?
3 give away money to their family / keep all the money for themselves?
4 eat in expensive restaurants / almost never go out?

b) 📟 Read and / or listen to this text about Bert Dunstan and mark the statements below *T* (True) or *F* (False).

TWO YEARS AGO Bert Dunstan won £12,000,000 on the National Lottery. Today he is dead. The 53-year-old factory worker was found lying lifeless on the sofa at his home last weekend.

When Bert won his fortune, he immediately gave up his £200-a-week job at the local chocolate factory and bought a luxurious new house. However, he did not immediately head for the sun on a Caribbean holiday or a round-the-world cruise, as others have done; instead, he packed his family of seven into one of his new cars and took them camping in Scotland.

Bert always liked his food and, instead of giving his only daughter, Sally, part of his winnings, he employed her as a full-time cook on a salary of £500 a week. 'I used to cook him three big meals every day: burgers, steak and chips were his favourites.' But Sally doesn't think Bert died through overeating: 'He just seemed to lose interest in life.'

Chloe Godwin, a psychologist who specialises in the effects that winning a large amount of money can have on people, says 'For some people the most terrible thing that can happen to them is change. This is why people have problems when they get married or pass exams. It's nice to win a few thousand pounds, but you shouldn't have so much that you move too far away from the life you've got.'

Certainly other lottery winners have had their problems: one of them left the country because of the publicity and because her family were fighting over the money. Another left his wife of 40 years and gave her nothing – the ticket was in *his* name, after all!

Losing can be just as bad, though: Freddie McMahon actually went mad when a group of people at his office won the jackpot – and he had refused to join them the week before.

So, whichever way you look at it, you just can't win!

1 Bert died two years after winning the lottery. ..*T*.
2 He spent some of the money on a new car. .....
3 He only gave his daughter £500. .....
4 Sally thinks that Bert ate himself to death. .....
5 The psychologist says that people find it very difficult when they have big changes in their lives. .....
6 One person left the country partly because of her relatives. .....
7 A husband and wife bought a winning lottery ticket together and then he left her. .....
8 Freddie McMahon went mad over a lottery ticket. .....

Pronunciation

/ʌ/

> **LOOK!**
> The sound /ʌ/ can be spelt in different ways:
> done   lunch   tough
> /ʌ/   /ʌ/   /ʌ/

10 a) Find and underline nine words in the box which contain /ʌ/.

public	stomach	burn
luxury	cough	rough
through	money	woman
push	enough	budget
tongue	encourage	huge

b) 📟 Listen to the words and repeat them.

c) Complete the gaps in these sentences with one of the words.

1 There's a ..*public*.......... telephone over there.

2 Have you had .... cake?

3 Ow! I've bitten my .... !

4 My mother tried to .... me to apply for the job.

5 Don't go swimming today because the sea's too ....

6 Ian hit me in the ....

7 Could you lend me some .... ?

8 Many years ago, chocolate used to be a ....

9 Has your department planned its .... for next year?

module 10

Past Perfect or Past Simple

1 Complete the gaps in these sentences with the best form of the verb in brackets (in each sentence one verb should be in the Past Perfect and the other(s) in the Past Simple).

a When the film _started_ (start) Beth realised she _'d seen_ (see) it before.

b I .... (be) surprised to find that Mr Cole .... (leave) the city the day before.

c Helen .... (feel) much better after she .... (have) a good sleep.

d The rain .... (stop) by the time we .... (get) to the beach.

e Melissa .... (be) angry because her brother .... (eat) all the chocolates.

f When Julia .... (meet) Scott she .... (not realise) he .... (be married) before.

g Geoff .... (not see) his parents for fifteen years so he .... (feel) rather nervous at the airport.

h The jazz singer .... (sing) an old blues song that I .... (never hear) before.

i When I .... (write) the letter I .... (post) it straightaway.

j Before Marti .... (become) Mrs Stephens' personal assistant she .... (work) as a receptionist.

k After Sarah .... (know) Alan for a few months he .... (ask) her to have dinner with him.

Present Perfect or Past Perfect

2 a) Tick (✓) the correct ending for each of these sentences.

1 Greg felt terrified because
  a he's never flown before.
  b he'd never flown before. ✓

2 How's Susan?
  a I haven't seen her for ages.
  b I hadn't seen her for ages.

3 The group *Just Girls* are breaking up and
  a they've only been together for 3 months.
  b they'd only been together for 3 months.

4 We were all very tired because
  a we've just travelled back from Florida.
  b we'd just travelled back from Florida.

5 It's the best restaurant
  a I've ever been to.
  b I'd ever been to.

6 The whole country was in shock because
  a the President has died.
  b the President had died.

7 It was the first time Juventus
  a have lost a match.
  b had lost a match.

8 What's the matter?
  a You've been depressed all week.
  b You'd been depressed all week.

b) Complete these sentences with your own ideas (use either the Present Perfect or the Past Perfect).

1 This is the best meal ....

2 It was the first time ....

3 Dave was surprised because ....

4 I'm not very hungry because ....

5 Sue played really badly because ....

6 The room was very cold because ....

Reported statements

3 a) Complete the sentences with a statement from the speech bubbles. Sometimes there are two possibilities.

Ten people have been killed in a bomb attack.

I practised eight hours every day.

The world is flat.

I've just got married.

Stephen's doing very well at maths.

You can be anything you want to be!

I'm sure I heard somebody in the garden, Inspector.

People in Brazil use the Internet more than anyone.

It'll rain overnight.

1 When I interviewed Mrs Taylor she said that *she was sure she'd heard somebody in the garden* .

2 On the weather forecast last night they said ....
....

3 Stephen's teacher told us ....
....

4 When I was young my father told me ....
....

5 They said on the news this morning that ....
....

6 600 years ago people thought that ....
....

7 I've just been reading an article in *Computer Monthly* which said that ....
....

8 My ex-boyfriend sent me a letter saying that ....
....

9 Wayne Rider, the new tennis star, said that when he was young ....
....

b) 🔲 Listen to some statements and use the prompts to report them.

You hear:

I'm tired. Jack said …

You say:

Jack said he was tired.

Reported questions

4 a) Clare has just arrived at San Francisco airport, where her friend Josh is meeting her. Clare took a long time to go through customs. Report the questions that she was asked.

What happened? Why are you so late?

Oh, I had a terrible time in customs. They asked me so many questions …

1 Where are you from?
   He asked me where I was from

2 Are you travelling alone?
   ....

3 Did you pack your suitcases yourself?
   ....

4 Have you got any hand luggage?
   ....

5 Did you get off the plane at the stopover in Amsterdam?
   ....
   ....

6 How long will you be in the country?
   ....

7 Where are you going to stay?
   ....

8 How much money have you brought with you?
   ....

b) 🔲 Listen to the questions and report them.

You hear:

Where are you from?

You say:

He asked me where I was from.

say and *tell*

> LOOK!
> - *I **told** t̶o̶ **Fran** that I'd be late.*
>   *tell + object*
> - *I **said** F̶r̶a̶n̶ I'd be late.*
>   *say without object*
> - *I **said to** Fran that I'd be late.*
>   *say + to + object*

5 Five of these sentences have mistakes. Find the mistakes and correct them.

a Sorry, what did you t̶e̶l̶l̶? *say*

b The press report said the President had been in an accident.

c Matthew hasn't told his boss that he's leaving yet.

d Roseanne's father said her she should be more polite.

e Danny told he was going to the USA.

f Tell to your brother that you're sorry.

g Mr Stuart said a lot of interesting things about the new plans.

h Could you say me your name again, please.

Vocabulary

Weather phrases

6 a) Match a weather phrase from column A with a result from column B.

A	B
1 It was a dark, stormy night	a so I put the washing out to dry.
2 There was thick fog	b so old Mrs Lampeter had to walk carefully.
3 There was a very strong wind	c so I hurried home from work and stayed in front of the fire.
4 The snow was a metre deep	d so everybody put on extra sweaters and scarves.
5 The streets were very slippery	e so we decided not to go sailing.
6 It was freezing cold	f and the grass was white and sparkling in the sun.
7 It was pouring with rain	g so Bud had to drive slowly because he couldn't see.
8 There was a warm breeze	h so we had to clear the path before we could go out.
9 It was a boiling hot day	i and the children got very wet.
10 It was a clear, frosty morning	j so they closed the car windows and turned on the air conditioning.

1 ..c..   2 ....   3 ....   4 ....   5 ....
6 ....   7 ....   8 ....   9 ....   10 ....

b) Now cover the phrases (1–10) and test yourself. Look at the sentences below and complete the gap with the missing word.

1 It was *freezing*............ cold.

2 There was a very .... wind.

3 There was .... fog.

4 It was a .... hot day.

5 The streets were very ....

6 It was a dark, ... night.

7 It was .... with rain.

8 It was a clear, ... morning.

9 The snow was a metre ....

10 There was a warm ....

Listen and read

Sherlock Holmes

In all the stories about the famous detective Sherlock Holmes, the storyteller is his assistant, Dr Watson. Inspector Lestrade is a detective from Scotland Yard.

7 a) 🖭 Read and / or listen to this extract from *The Six Busts of Napoleon* and answer the questions.

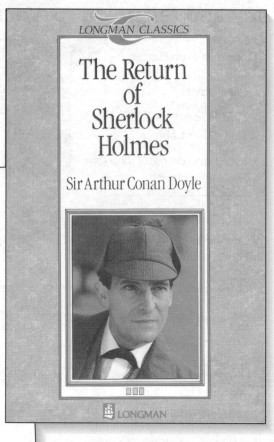

LONGMAN CLASSICS

The Return of Sherlock Holmes

Sir Arthur Conan Doyle

LONGMAN

Lestrade and I woke up at half past ten. Holmes was waiting for us. He told me to bring my gun and I saw him pick up his favourite strong walking stick before we left the house.

We quickly drove to Chiswick, and Holmes took us to a large house in a dark street. I thought that the people inside must have already gone to bed because the house was so dark and quiet.

'I'm glad it's not raining,' said Holmes quietly. 'We may have to wait a long time. We mustn't smoke and we must be very quiet, but I hope we are going to discover something tonight.'

We waited for five minutes but we didn't have to wait much longer. The garden gate suddenly opened and a man ran quickly down the garden path towards the house. It was so dark and he moved so quickly that it was impossible to see his face. He disappeared into the darkness and we waited in silence.

The next thing we heard was the sound of a window opening very slowly, then we saw a small light inside the front room of the house.

'Let's go to the open window, then we can catch him as he comes out,' said Lestrade.

But before we could move, the man had come outside again. In the light we could see that he had something white under his arm. He looked round to see if anyone was watching him. Then there was a sudden crash as he broke the thing against the wall. He was so busy that he didn't see the three of us coming towards him. Holmes jumped on his back and he fell to the ground heavily. Lestrade and I quickly ran to help Holmes. I had my gun ready and soon it was impossible for the man to escape.

---

1 Does it take place during the day or night?

2 How many people are involved in this part of the story?

b) Listen and / or read again and mark these statements *T* (true) or *F* (false).

1 Holmes and Watson know the situation will be dangerous. ..*T*.

2 They got wet while they waited. .....

3 A man comes out of the house after five minutes. .....

4 Watson recognises the man. .....

5 The man climbs into the house through a window. .....

6 The man steals something from the house, then breaks it. .....

7 The man attacks Sherlock Holmes. .....

Pronunciation

Connected speech: links between words

> **LOOK!**
>
> Here is an extract from the Sherlock Holmes story *The Six Busts of Napoleon*. Notice how we link some words: **Lestrade and I**
>
> consonant + vowel
>
> 'Lestrade and I woke up at half past ten. Holmes was waiting for us. He told me to bring my gun and I saw him pick up his favourite strong walking stick before we left the house.'

8 a) Mark the links between words in this paragraph from the Sherlock Holmes story.

> But before we could move, the man had come outside again. In the light we could see that he had something white under his arm. He looked round to see if anyone was watching him. Then there was a sudden crash as he broke the thing against the wall. He was so busy that he didn't see the three of us coming towards him. Holmes jumped on his back and he fell to the ground heavily. Lestrade and I quickly ran to help Holmes. I had my gun ready and soon it was impossible for the man to escape.

b) 🖭 Listen to the paragraph and repeat each phrase, giving special attention to the links.

Grammar snack

Definite article for shared knowledge

> **LOOK!**
>
> We use *the* when it is clear to the reader or listener which person or thing we are talking about:
>
> • '*Are you coming to the pub?*'
>   (The speaker and the listener both know which pub.)
>
> • '*There's a nice pub about 10 minutes away.*'
>   (The listener doesn't know the pub.)
>
> • '*Who's that at the door?*'
>   (The speaker and the listener know that this means the front door of the house they are in.)
>
> • '*I heard a door open.*'
>   (The speaker doesn't know which one.)

9 Here is the beginning of a Sherlock Holmes story, *The Golden Glasses*. Dr Watson is telling the story. Complete the gaps with *a / an* or *the*.

> It was (1) ...*a*..... very stormy night near the end of November. Sherlock Holmes and I were reading by (2) .... fire. It was late, and most people were in bed. There was no one outside in (3) .... street.
>
> Holmes put down his book, and said, 'I'm glad that we don't have to go out tonight, Watson.'
>
> 'So am I,' I replied.
>
> Just then we heard (4) .... carriage stop outside (5) .... house. Someone was getting out. I went to (6) .... window and looked outside.
>
> 'Someone is coming here,' I said.
>
> 'I wonder who it is,' Holmes answered.
>
> Very soon we knew who our visitor was. It was (7) .... young detective from Scotland Yard. Holmes and I had helped him with some cases in the past.
>
> 'Come and sit down by (8) .... fire,' said Holmes. 'It's (9) .... very cold, wet night. I think you must have (10) .... interesting case for me!'

Improve your writing

Time expressions for telling stories

10 **a)** Sheila keeps a diary about what happens to her each day. Read these extracts about how she met Gregory, a Russian man studying English. Complete the gaps with a suitable word or phrase from the box. (You will need to use some of them more than once.)

after	afterwards	during	for	until	when
while	in the end	at first			

Saturday 9th September

Sue's party – I felt a bit shy (1) ..at first........... because I didn't know anyone. Then Sue introduced me to one of her students, a man called Gregory, from Moscow. I chatted to him quite a lot – his English is really good!

Tuesday 12th September

I went to the library and (2) .... I was looking for a book I saw Gregory, the guy from Sue's party. He was doing his English homework and (3) .... he saw me, he asked me if I could help him with some words he didn't know. I sat down with him (4) .... a few minutes and helped him finish the exercises. (5) ...., he insisted on buying me a coffee, and we chatted (6) .... hours – (7) .... the coffee shop shut, in fact!

Wednesday 13th September

Gregory phoned and asked me to go to a concert with him (8) .... work tomorrow night. (9) .... I wasn't sure, because of having to get up early the next day, but Gregory explained that it was a famous Russian pianist, so (10) .... I said I'd go.

Thursday 14th September

We had a great evening. The music was brilliant and I really enjoyed being with Gregory. (11) .... the interval we met some of G's friends, and (12) .... we all went to a wine bar in town. G. brought me home and we've arranged to meet again at the weekend. I'm really looking forward to seeing him again ...

LOOK!

These pairs of time expressions can be easily confused:

- **After** the lesson, we went for a drink.
  After + noun

- **Afterwards**, we took a taxi home.
  Afterwards + clause

- It was a terrible day. **First** I missed the bus, then I spilt coffee all over my skirt.
  First is used to show the order of events or instructions.

- I hated my boss **at first**, but now we get on well.
  At first refers to a point of time before another point of time.

- **At the end** of the film she died.
  At the end = when something finishes.

- **In the end** I agreed to help them.
  In the end = finally, after a period of time.

b) Complete the gaps in these sentences with a word or phrase from the box.

after	in the end	first	~~at the end~~	at first
afterwards				

1 *At the end*........ of the concert, Liam took his shirt off and threw it into the audience.

2 .... I pulled the injured man out of the car and then I called the ambulance.

3 I thought Phil was joking .... but then I realised he was serious.

4 I said good-bye and put the phone down. ...., I remembered something I'd forgotten to say.

5 Sara didn't really want to come on holiday with us, but .... she agreed to come.

6 .... the long journey to my grandparents' house, I just wanted to go to bed.

module 11

Obligation and permission

1 Complete the gaps in these sentences with a word or phrase from the box.

> should   shouldn't   can   can't   must   mustn't
> ought   havé   don't have   are allowed
> aren't allowed

a   You .... *have* .... to leave your keys at reception when you go out of the hotel.

b   I think people .... spend more time with their families and less time at work.

c   Passengers .... to walk around the plane when it is taking off.

d   Candidates .... to take a dictionary into the exam, but they can't take in a grammar book.

e   You .... buy alcohol in a pub unless you're over 18.

f   You look really tired. I think you .... to take a day off.

g   Monday's a holiday so we .... to go to school until Tuesday.

h   You .... ride a bicycle on the motorway – it's very dangerous.

i   Guests .... have breakfast any time between 7.00 and 9.00 a.m.

j   I know I .... really smoke so much, but it helps me to relax.

k   You .... sign your name in this book when you enter or leave the building.

2 Here are the answers to some questions about rules. First decide if they are about a language class (LC), a library (LIB) or a sports club (SC) and then use the prompts to make complete questions.

a   You can borrow up to three books at a time. _LIB_
   How many books / allowed / at a time?
   How many books am I allowed to borrow at a time ?

b   Yes, you can book up to two days in advance. ....
   Can / aerobics classes / in advance?
   .... ?

c   You're allowed to keep them for three weeks. ....
   How long / allowed / books?
   .... ?

d   Yes, first you take a short written test, then there's an interview with a teacher. ....
   I / have to / test?
   .... ?

e   Yes, bring a passport-sized photo for your membership card. ....
   Should / a photo?
   .... ?

f   No, you don't have to – you can join for just six months if you like. ....
   I / have to / a whole year?
   .... ?

g   Well, if you miss too many, you won't get a certificate at the end of the course. ....
   How many classes / allowed?
   .... ?

Obligation and permission in the past

3 Reorder the words in these conversations. The first word is underlined.

a) Kim and Pieter are talking about a maths exam.

KIM: exam – to – calculator – <u>Were</u> – a – allowed – the – take – into – you ?

Were you allowed to take a calculator into the exam?

PIETER: weren't – <u>No</u> – we

....

KIM: did – answer – many – have – <u>How</u> – questions – to – you ?

....

....

PIETER: three – <u>We</u> – do – in – had – hours – twenty – to

....

b) Patrizia and Italo are talking about a Summer camp.

PATRIZIA: up – allowed – you – late – to – <u>Were</u> – stay ?

.... ?

ITALO: campfire – we – by – midnight – <u>Yeah</u> – until – sit – the – could

....

....

PATRIZIA: get – early – you – up – <u>Did</u> – to – have ?

.... ?

ITALO: to – 9 – we – <u>No</u> – up – didn't – until – get – have

....

c) Mona is talking to Vanessa about Vanessa's daughter, Francoise.

MONA: America – a – <u>Did</u> – have – Francoise – time – in – good ?

....

.... ?

VANESSA: six – week – to – she – work – <u>No</u> – a – days – had

....

....

MONA: terrible – <u>That's</u> !

.... !

VANESSA: allowed – us – to – wasn't – she – phone – <u>And</u>

....

4 These people are talking about their lives when they were about fourteen. Change the sentences (if necessary) so that they are true for you.

a MARIA: I had to wear white gloves and a hat to school.
   I didn't have to wear gloves or a hat .

b JOHN: I couldn't stay up after 8.00 p.m. during the week.

   ....

c LISBETH: We were allowed to wear whatever we wanted at school.

   ....

d PAOLO: I had to go to church twice on Sundays.

   ....

e ANNA: I could go out to play with my friends whenever I wanted to.

   ....

f JANE: We weren't allowed to speak in the corridors at school.

   ....

g JUDIT: We could call our teachers by their first names.

   ....

h MARK: I was allowed to watch any TV programmes I wanted.

   ....

must and have to

5 Complete the gaps in these sentences with a word or phrase from the box.

must   mustn't (x2)   have to   don't have to (x2)
had to   didn't have to

a You ......*mustn't*...... smoke in the library.

b It's free to get in: you .... pay.

c I missed my train and I .... wait half an hour for the next one.

d It's not a direct flight to New Zealand: you .... change planes at Bangkok.

e There were only two people in front of me in the queue so I .... wait long.

f Don't cry, Jessica – you .... play with Jon if you don't want to.

g Children .... walk on the railway line.

h I .... remember to post this letter.

make and *let*

LOOK!

Let (permission)

• *My sister **lets her children do** whatever they like.*
(*let* + object + base form)
= My sister allows her children to do whatever they like.

Make (obligation)

• *My mother **makes me clean** my room every week.*
(*make* + object + base form)
= I have to clean my room every week (my mother tells me to do it).

6 Match a sentence from column A with one from column B and complete the gaps with the best form of *let* or *make*.

A

a   My boss was very understanding when my mother was ill.

b   The doctor was very patient.

c   Our teacher is really strict.

d   Lucy was delayed at the airport

e   Don and Rita were very generous.

f   There's a really good documentary on TV tonight.

g   That woman in the sales department is very difficult to please.

B

1   The customs officer .... her open her suitcase.

2   She .... me write two of my reports again.

3   Don't .... me forget to video it.

4   He .... us work very hard.

5   He ..*let*.... me have two days off work.

6   She .... me talk about all my problems.

7   They .... us spend a week in their house in the mountains.

a ...*5*... b .... c .... d .... e .... f .... g ....

Spelling and pronunciation

School / university subjects

7 **a)** Each of the subjects in the box has a spelling mistake. Correct the mistake.

mathmatics	giography	biologie	fisics	cemistry	histery
langauges	litterature	information tecnology		sosciology	
sychology	filosophy	phisical education		midia studies	
religous studies	economicks				

b) 🎧 Listen to the words and mark the stressed syllables ● and the unstressed syllables ○,
e.g. mathematics.
○ ●○

c) Complete these sentences so that they are true for you.

1   My favourite subject is / was
....
because ....
....

2   I am / was very good at
....

3   I hate / hated
....
because ....
....

4   I am / was hopeless at
....

5   I find / found
.... very difficult.

6   .... is / was very boring.

7   I like / liked
.... but I'm not / I wasn't very good at it.

8   I find / found
.... really interesting.

Vocabulary

Transport: noun + noun

8 Pair a noun from box A with a noun from box B and complete the gaps in the sentences.

A	B
taxi crash season speed bus parking petrol traffic	ticket limit fare jam rank helmet meter station

a   I put £2 in the *parking* *meter*........, so we can leave the car here until 5.30.

b   I'm sorry I'm late. There was a terrible .... near the football ground, because of all the people coming out of the match.

c   The last bus has gone, but there's a .... in the next street: it won't cost much to go to your hotel.

d   If you're going to take the train to work every day, it's cheaper to buy a ....

e   I think we should stop at the next .... and fill the car up for the journey.

f   It's very dangerous to ride a motorbike without a ....

g   Don't drive so fast! The ....'s 60 mph on this road.

h   I've only got a £20-note: could you lend me 90p for my .... ?

Grammar snack

Prepositions of movement

9 **a)** Look at the arrow in the pictures (1–10). Choose one of the phrases (a–j) below to say where the arrow goes.

1 ...*d*....   2 ....

3 ....   4 ....

5 ....   6 ....

7 ....   8 ....

9 ....   10 ....

a   along the river
b   through the gate
c   past the house
d   into the house
e   through the house
f   across the river
g   towards the house
h   out of the house
i   round the house
j   away from the house

b) Look at this plan of an airport terminal and complete the gaps in the directions below with a suitable preposition.

1 (At the entrance) Are there any cash dispensers here?

Yes, you go ......*past*....... the post office and bank and they're just on the right.

2 (At the cash dispenser) Is there anywhere I can post this letter?

If you go .... the entrance, there's a letter box in the wall next to the Post Office.

3 (At the letter box) Excuse me, where can I get a trolley?

Go .... the terminal building and they're just outside on your right.

4 (At the trolley park) Could you tell me where the Quantas check-in desk is, please?

Yes. Go .... the entrance and you'll see lots of check-in desks in front of you. Quantas is the third one.

5 (At the Quantas check-in desk) Where are the telephones, please?

Go .... passport control and .... the cafe: they're just on your right.

6 (In the cafe) Is there anywhere to get something to eat in the departure lounge?

Yes, there's quite a big restaurant. When you've gone .... passport control and security, go .... the lounge and you'll see it.

7 (In the restaurant) Could you tell me where the toilets are?

Yes, go .... the back of the duty free area over there, and you'll see them.

Grammar snack

-ing forms as nouns

> **LOOK!**
> • It's dangerous to drive when you're tired.
> • Driving when you're tired is dangerous.
> Notice: *Driving* is now a noun, and is the subject of the sentence.

10 Look at the sentences below and rewrite them using an *-ing* form.

a   It's compulsory to wear a seatbelt in a car.
Wearing a seatbelt in a car is compulsory .

b   It's quite easy to buy a gun.
....

c   It's possible to park on the pavement.
....

d   It's forbidden to wear shorts in church.
....

e   It's common to live with your parents until you get married.
....

f   It's difficult to get a divorce.
....

g   It's not a good idea to walk alone at night.
....

h   It's permitted to get married at the age of 14.
....

i   It isn't compulsory to wear a crash helmet on a motorbike.
....

j   It is illegal to buy drugs.
....

Improve your writing

Linking words

11 Read the text and circle the correct linking word.

Surrogate Mothers:
IS THE PRICE TOO HIGH?

Nowadays science has made it possible for a couple who can't have children to pay a woman to have their baby for them. These 'surrogate' mothers sign a contract promising to give the baby to the couple as soon as it is born, in return for a large sum of money. (1) *However / Also*, this business arrangement does not always work well in practice and, (2) *despite this / as a result*, there have been a number of 'horror stories' in the newspapers recently.

People have strong feelings on both sides. Some say that it is every woman's right to have a child. (3) *Although / What is more*, a surrogate mother can often save an unhappy marriage and make some money for herself. (4) *Therefore / Despite this*, many people are against this practice. They say that (5) *although / besides* they understand the heartache of a childless woman, having a baby is not an automatic right. They feel the whole thing is completely unnatural and (6) *for this reason / also* should not be allowed. (7) *Besides / However*, they ask what will happen to the child when he or she is old enough to know the truth. This could have a terrible effect on their mental and emotional development. I feel that this last point is particularly important and (8) *therefore / what is more*, I tend to agree that surrogacy is wrong, or at least that there should be stricter rules about it.

module 12

could have / should have / would have

1 Look at the pictures and match them to the captions below.

a 'Oh well, they wouldn't have had room for my luggage, anyway.'
b 'What do you mean, you gave him your sweets? I'd have hit him.'
c 'Darling, you could have hurt yourself.'
d 'Oh well, it's not too bad – we could have lost everything.'
e 'I knew I shouldn't have gone to that hairdresser.'
f 'You should have told me your boss was a vegetarian.'

1 ..*e*.....   2 ....   3 ....   4 ....   5 ....   6 ....

2 Complete the gaps in these sentences with a phrase from the box, and the best form of the verb in brackets.

> could have (x2)   couldn't have   should have (x2)
> shouldn't have   would have (x2)   wouldn't have

a Oh no, I've forgotten Marcel's address. I knew I
should have written .... (*write*) it down.

b Why didn't you buy them that picture? I'm sure
they .... (*like*) it.

c We did our best to catch the train: we
.... (*run*) any faster.

d You .... (*listen*) to Paul.
You know he has some stupid ideas.

e I like Kristin's new motorbike, but I
.... (*buy*) a bigger one.

f Look where you're going – we were really close to
that car. We .... (*have*) an
accident.

g You were right not to tell her the truth about Brian: she
.... (*believe*) you, anyway.

h Rupert .... (*be*) a great
pianist, but he didn't practise enough.

i The room was a terrible mess when the men had
finished painting it. I .... (*do*)
it myself.

3 🔲 Listen to these sentences and repeat what you hear (circle the correct phrase).

a *You shouldn't walk /* (*You shouldn't have walked*) home
so late at night.

b *We could invite / We could have invited* our teacher to
the picnic on Saturday.

c Do you still have a headache? *You should take / You
should have taken* an aspirin.

d I'm glad you bought a cake. *I wouldn't have / I
wouldn't have had* time to make one.

e Has Jon really gone running in this rain? *I'd stay / I'd
have stayed* at home.

f Mum and I waited for nearly an hour. *We couldn't
wait / We couldn't have waited* any longer.

Past sentences with *if*

4 Look at these half sentences and match a first half from column A with a second half from column B.

A

a If I hadn't lost my passport

b If Sara and I had stayed longer in Paris

c If we'd booked our theatre tickets in advance

d If Greta hadn't spent £10,000 on a new car

e If Malcolm had stopped smoking

f If my uncle lived near the airport

g If it hadn't rained

h If you hadn't taken so long to get ready

B

1 she'd have enough money to pay her rent.

2 I'd have stayed at his house on my way to Germany.

3 I'd be on the plane to Tunisia.

4 we wouldn't have had to queue outside.

5 we could have taken the children to the zoo.

6 we wouldn't have missed our bus.

7 he wouldn't have such a terrible cough.

8 we'd have visited Euro Disney.

a ..*3*..   b ......   c ......   d ......   e ......   f ......   g ......   h ......

5 Rewrite the following sentences so that they mean the same, using a past sentence with *if*.

a Kristin moved to San Francisco and that's how she met Ralph.
Kristin *wouldn't have met Ralph if she hadn't moved to San Francisco* .

b You didn't wear a jumper. That's why you're cold.
If you ....

c Josh was very tired and so he lost his temper.
Josh ....
....

d Sam didn't do his homework, so he doesn't know the answer.
If Sam ....
....

e My hair looks terrible. That's because I didn't go to my usual hairdresser.
If I ....
....

f I don't have a very well-paid job because I haven't done a computer course.
If I'd ....
....

g Alice wasn't at home last night. That's why she didn't get your message.
Alice ....
....

h The store manager knew Ruth's father. That's why he gave her the job.
If the store manager ....
....

6 Complete these sentences with your own ideas.

a If you'd been more careful doing the washing up ....
....
....

b If I'd put the correct stamp on the letter ....
....
....

c If we'd put more salt and pepper on the food ....
....
....
....

d If the weather had been better last weekend ....
....
....

e If my mother hadn't lent me some money ....
....
....

Grammar snack

Verb + object + infinitive

> **LOOK!**
>
> • *The doctor **told me to drink** more water.*
>   (*tell* + object + infinitive)
>
> • *The doctor **told me not to drink** so much beer.*
>   (*tell* + object + *not* + infinitive)
>
> Other verbs that follow this pattern:
> *advise   ask   persuade   remind   teach   want*

7 a) Rewrite these sentences so that they mean the same, using the verb in brackets.

1 Doug said to me, 'be more careful.' (*tell*)
  Doug told me to be more careful .

2 'Juliet, please stay,' Jim said. (*want*)
  Jim ....

3 My father gave me driving lessons last year. (*teach*)
  My father ....

4 The local people said we shouldn't drink the water.
  (*advise*)
  The local people ....
  ....

5 'Sarah, could you get me some aspirin,' John said.
  (*ask*)
  John ....

6 After a lot of discussion, the travel agent agreed to give Toni and Jo a discount. (*persuade*)
  Toni and Jo ....
  ....

7 'Don't forget to lock the back door,' my mother told me. (*remind*)
  My mother ....

8 'Don't touch the computer,' we said to the children.
  (*tell*)
  We ....

9 'I think you should go to the police,' Ian said to Martin. (*advise*)
  Ian ....

10 'Please don't make so much noise,' Todd said to his neighbour. (*ask*)
  Todd ....

b) Complete these sentences so that they are true for you.

1 If someone was visiting my city, I'd advise ....
  ....

2 It's not easy to persuade me ....
  ....

3 People always have to remind me ....
  ....

4 If I had a daughter, I'd want her ....
  ....

5 I sometimes ask my English teacher to ....
  ....

Jazz chant

Verbs that describe behaviour and reactions

8 a) Read the jazz chant and complete the gaps with the best form of the verb in brackets, adding a preposition if necessary.

Tom persuaded his mother (1) *to lend* (lend) him her car

And promised (2) .... (get) back by eight

His mother agreed (3) .... (give) him the keys

And trusted him not to be late.

When the police brought him home at a quarter to two

She ran down the stairs from her bed

'**W**e suspect this young man (4) .... (tell) us lies'

She refused (5) .... (believe) what they said.

She insisted (6) .... (hear) his side of the tale

He admitted (7) .... (drive) too fast

But strongly denied (8) .... (have) too much to drink

'**M**y first glass of beer was my last.'

The officers threatened (9) .... (take) him away

His mum wouldn't let them and she

Suggested (10) .... (discuss) the case the next day

They did, and they let him go free.

b) 🔲 Listen to the jazz chant and say it with the cassette.

Vocabulary

Using the dictionary: revision

> **re·act** /riˈækt/ v [I] **1** to behave in a particular way because of some-thing that has happened or something that has been said to you: [**+ to**] *How did Wilson react to your idea?*
> **react against** sth *phr v* [T] to show that you dislike someone else's rules or way of doing something by deliberately doing the opposite: *Feminists reacted against women's traditional roles.*

LOOK!

When you look a word up in the dictionary it shows you:
• the pronunciation /riˈækt/ including the main stress (shown by ')
• the grammar, e.g. *v* = verb, *n* = noun
• if a noun is countable [C] or uncountable [U]
• if there is a preposition which follows it, e.g. react (to, against)
• the meaning, and gives example sentences.

9 **a)** Use these extracts from the *Longman Dictionary of Contemporary English* to complete the chart below. Mark the main stress ●.

ad·vice /ədˈvaɪs/ *n* [U] an opinion you give someone about what they should do: [**+ on/about**] *There's lots of advice in the book on baby care.* |**give advice** *Can you give me some advice about buying a house?*
ad·vi·sa·ble /ədˈvaɪzəbəl/ *adj* something that is advisable should be done in order to avoid problems: *For heavy smokers, regular medical checks are advisable.*|
ad·vise /ədˈvaɪz/ *v* to tell someone what you think they should do: **advise sb to do sth** *Passengers are advised not to leave their bags unattended.*|

de·cide /dɪˈsaɪd/ *v* to make a choice or judgment about something **decide to do sth** *Tina's decided to go to Prague for her holidays.*|
de·ci·sion /dɪˈsɪʒən/ *n* [C] a choice or judgment that you make after a period of discussion or thought: *The judge's decision is final.* |**make/take a decision** (=decide) *The committee will make its decision this week.*|
de·ci·sive /dɪˈsaɪsɪv/ *adj* good at making decisions quickly and with confidence: *a decisive leader*|

ig·no·rance /ˈɪɡnərəns/ *n* [U] no knowledge or information about something: *My mistake was caused by ignorance.*
ig·no·rant /ˈɪɡnərənt/ *adj* not knowing facts or information that you ought to know: *an ignorant man*| [**+ about**] *I'm very ignorant about politics.*|
ig·nore /ɪɡˈnɔː/ *v* to behave as if you had not heard or seen someone or something: *Either she didn't see me or she deliberately ignored me.*|

know¹ /nəʊ/ *v past tense* knew / njuː/ *past participle* known /nəʊn/ to have information about something: *Who knows the answer?*|
knowl·edge /ˈnɒlɪdʒ/ *n* [U] the facts, skills, and under-standing that you have gained through learning or experience: [**+ of**] *His knowledge of ancient civilizations is wonderful.*|
knowl·edge·a·ble /ˈnɒlɪdʒəbəl/ *adj* knowing a lot: [**+ about**] *Graham's very knowledgeable about wines.*

so·lu·tion /səˈluːʃən/ *n* [C] a way of solving a problem or dealing with a difficult situation|[**+ to**] *There are no simple solutions to the problem of overpopulation.* **find a solution** *The governments are trying to find a peaceful solution.*
solve /sɒlv/ *v* to find or provide a way of dealing with a problem: *Charlie thinks money will solve all his problems.*

verb	noun	adjective
advise	advice	
decide		
ignore		
know		
	solution	–

b) Circle the correct answer in these sentences.

1 After 'knowledge' we use the preposition (of)/ about.
2 'Advice' is a *countable / uncountable* noun.
3 The pronunciation of 'advice' and 'advise' is *the same / different*.
4 In 'ignore' the letter 'g' is *silent / not silent*.
5 After 'solution' we use the preposition *to / at*.
6 'Solution' is a *countable / uncountable* noun.
7 People *make / do* a decision.
8 The pronunciation of the first 'i' in 'decisive' and 'decision' is the *same / different*.

c) Complete the gaps in these sentences with the correct word (use the dictionary extracts).

1 It's not ___advisable___ to swim immediately after a big meal.
2 Pauline's very knowledgeable .... jazz music.
3 Have you .... a solution to your problem yet?
4 The teacher .... Jim's question and continued talking.
5 I'm not very .... when I go shopping: it takes me a long time to choose clothes.
6 Could you give my daughter .... advice about music lessons?
7 The teacher was shocked by the children's .... : they knew nothing about the history of their country.
8 The solution .... the problem isn't easy.
9 The journalist's .... of the political situation was very good.

Real life

Starting and finishing conversations

10 **a)** Match the speech bubbles to make complete phrases for starting and finishing conversations.

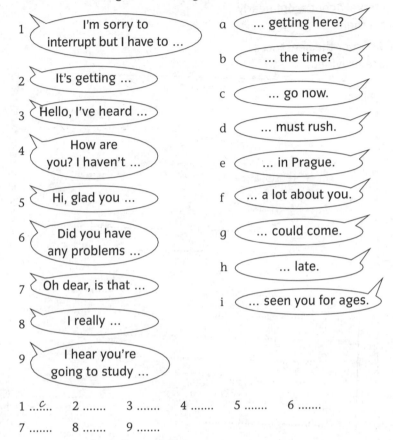

1 I'm sorry to interrupt but I have to ...

2 It's getting ...

3 Hello, I've heard ...

4 How are you? I haven't ...

5 Hi, glad you ...

6 Did you have any problems ...

7 Oh dear, is that ...

8 I really ...

9 I hear you're going to study ...

a ... getting here?

b ... the time?

c ... go now.

d ... must rush.

e ... in Prague.

f ... a lot about you.

g ... could come.

h ... late.

i ... seen you for ages.

1 ...c.. 2 .... 3 .... 4 .... 5 .... 6 ....
7 .... 8 .... 9 ....

b) Now write the complete phrases in the correct column in the chart.

Starting conversations	Finishing conversations
1 *Hello, I've heard a lot about you.*	6
2	7
3	8
4	9
5	

c) Look at the following situations, which take place at a party. Choose the best phrase (1–9 above) for each situation.

1 You're having a party. The doorbell rings, you open the door and see two good friends. What do you say?

Hi, glad you could come ....

2 It's a cold night and there's ice on the roads. You know they came by car. As you take their coats, what do you say?

....

3 As you go into the party, your friend Simon comes up and sees your guests. It's a long time since he has seen them. What does he say?

....

4 You take your friends into the party and introduce them to your sister. What does your sister say?

....

5 Later at the party, one of your guests introduces his girlfriend to you. You don't know very much about her, except that she's going to study in Prague. What do you say?

....

6 It's 11.30. You're in the middle of a conversation and a friend who lives a long way away comes up to you. What does he say?

....

7 It's 1 o'clock. You've been having a very interesting conversation with one of your guests when she suddenly looks at her watch. What does she say? (Two phrases together)

....

d) 📼 Listen to the situations and say the correct phrase.

You hear:

You're having a party. The doorbell rings and you see two good friends.

You say:

Hi, glad you could come.

Improve your writing

A letter to sort out a problem

11 **a)** Lucy Humphries booked a flight to Mexico City and paid by credit card. She received her ticket a few days later, but the dates on the ticket were wrong. She sent the ticket back to the travel agent's, but nearly two weeks have passed and she has not heard from them.

Lucy has written a letter to sort out the problem. Reorder the sentences below and write out the complete letter in the space provided.

> A week later, I received my credit card receipt and the ticket, but unfortunately the dates were wrong.

> That was 10 days ago, and I have heard nothing from you since then.

> You booked me onto a flight costing £425, which I paid by credit card.

> I look forward to hearing from you.

> As you can imagine, I am very concerned about this because I need to make other arrangements for my trip, which I cannot do until the dates are confirmed.

> Several weeks ago I telephoned your office to book a return flight to Mexico City, leaving on July 8th and returning on July 27th.

> I would therefore be grateful if you could look into this matter immediately.

> I immediately returned the ticket by registered post, with a note explaining the problem.

---

44 Barn Road
Nottingham NS4
May 29th 19-

The Manager
Eurotrips Travel Agent's

Dear Sir/Madam

....

....

....

....

....

....

....

....

....

....

....

....

....

....

....

Yours faithfully

L Humphries

---

b) In your notebook write a letter to sort out the problem below.
Use the letter above to help you and show your letter to your teacher.

> Three weeks ago, you booked a 4-week course at the *Success* Language School, 354 Liffey Road, Dublin DN6. A week ago, you had not received a receipt or confirmation of your place on the course. You phoned the school and left a message on the ansaphone, but you have still not heard anything.
>
> Before you write the letter, decide:
> • How many hours a day your course is: 3 / 4 / 5 ?
> • How you paid for the course: credit card / bank transfer?
> • The dates of your course.

Answer key

Introduction

Grammar terms

1

b	soup	g	telling	l	you
c	wet	h	don't	m	your
d	under	i	can't	n	because
e	never	j	the		
f	be	k	a		

Using a dictionary

2

b	a noun	d	a verb	f	a noun
c	an adjective	e	a noun	g	a noun

3

b	enjoyment	e	enjoyable
c	enjoy	f	trainee
d	training	g	trainer

module 1

Making questions

1 **a)**

2 Which part of Italy does she come from?
3 How did you meet her?
4 What does she do for a living?
5 When did she first come to England?
6 How well does she speak English?
7 Does she like London?
8 Has she got a flat here? / Does she have a flat here?

b)
1 When did you get married?
2 Where was your husband born?
3 Does your husband work?
4 Has he got any qualifications? / Does he have any qualifications?
5 How many children have you got? / How many children do you have?
6 How old are your children?
7 Do you know anybody in Australia?

Short answers

2

b Do you live with your family? Yes, I do.
c Do you live in an apartment? No we don't.
d Did you live in the same place when you were young? No, we didn't.
e Are your grandparents alive? No, they aren't. / No they're not.
f Have you got a car? No, I haven't.
g Can you understand English well? Yes, I can.
h Does your English teacher speak your language? No, s/he doesn't.

Question tags

3 **a)**

1	b	doesn't it?	2	a	aren't you?
	c	haven't they?		b	don't you?
	d	aren't they?		c	haven't you?
	e	are there?		d	do you?
				e	can't you?

Present Simple or Continuous

4

2 's going / is going
3 Do you smoke
4 do you work
5 do
6 'm working / am working
7 do you relax
8 sit
9 Are you doing
10 don't know
11 're suffering / are suffering
12 want

State verbs

5

2 has
3 costs
4 'm buying / am buying
5 doesn't want
6 understand
7 think
8 looks
9 don't have
10 're waiting / are waiting
11 don't know
12 's having / is having

Word order
Adverbs of frequency

6 **a)**

2 (Occasionally) my colleague Jo (occasionally) uses my computer (occasionally).
3 (Quite often) my classmate Carla (quite often) has lunch with me (quite often).
4 My boss is hardly ever in the office.
5 (Most of the time) my neighbours are very quiet (most of the time).
6 My sister-in-law Jenny nearly always phones me on Mondays.
7 Paul's relatives always visit us at Christmas.
8 Stephen hardly ever sees his ex-girlfriend.
9 Daryl, my flatmate, never cleans the bathroom.

Pronunciation

/ ə / (schwa)

7 a)

3	couple /ə/	8	foreign /ə/
4	brother-in-law /ə/	9	headteacher /ə/
5	photograph /ə/	10	neighbour /ə/
6	stranger /ə/	11	partner /ə/
7	relative /ə/	12	parent /ə/

c)

2 occasionally /ə/ /ə/   5 salesman /ə/

3 usually /ə/   6 catalogue /ə/

4 assistant /ə/ /ə/

The letter 's'

8 a)

/s/	/z/	/ɪz/
parents	spells	nieces
classmates	entertains	practises
hopes	relatives	acquaintances
works	colleagues	uses
	spends	pronounces

Grammar snack

both / neither

9 a)

2 a
3 b
4 b
5 a

b)

2 **Neither of** my neighbours is / are noisy.
3 Both my sister and my niece **spend** a lot of time cooking.
4 My colleagues Dan and Rob are quite lazy: neither of them **does** much work.
5 My best friend June and I **are both** learning a musical instrument.
6 Neither Ann **nor** Susan likes watching football.

Vocabulary

Activities with *do / play / go*

10 a)

do	play	go
• sport	• the drums	• cycling
• photography	• the guitar	• swimming
• gardening	• cards	• jogging
knitting	snooker	• skiing
• exercise	• a computer game	• dancing
• yoga	• volleyball	• walking

c)

2 a – playing   5 c – play
3 d – do, go   6 b – does
4 f – go

Improve your writing

Spelling of the *-ing* form

11

b paying   g hoping   l answering
c writing   h planning   m training
d seeing   i jogging   n growing
e beginning   j travelling   o driving
f faxing   k printing

Listen and read

Unusual lifestyles

12 a)

1 Gemma: singer
2 Raoul: assistant chef
3 Frank: crossword puzzle writer

b)

2 Raoul   7 Raoul
3 Frank   8 Frank
4 Gemma   9 Gemma
5 Frank   10 Raoul
6 Gemma

module 2

Past Simple or Continuous

1

b He was playing football and he fell over.
c We were sunbathing at the weekend and we stayed out too long.
d He was walking in the rain and he got very wet.
e They were staying in Florida when there was a terrible storm.
f She was travelling home from work and she left it on the bus.

2

2	was working	6	was
3	didn't hear	7	was training
4	was talking	8	broke
5	went	9	spent

3

a A: Penny told me you had an accident yesterday. What happened?
   B: We were driving home and another car stopped suddenly and we went into it.
   A: Was the other car alright?
   B: Yes, luckily we weren't going very fast.

b A: How did your brother get that scar on his hand?
   B: He got it while we were living in Italy.
   A: Oh, how?
   B: He was playing near the oven and he burnt his hand on the oven door.
   A: Ooh, nasty!

Pronunciation
Syllable stress in Past Simple forms

4

a)

3	●○ travelled	8	●○ changed	13	○●○ repeated
4	● looked	9	●○ practised	14	●○ started
5	○●○ reminded	10	●○ decided	15	● closed
6	● watched	11	○● improved		
7	● asked	12	○●○ received		

b)

1	*It happened yesterday.*	9	*We practised a lot.*
2	*I stopped it.*	10	*Irena decided to go.*
3	*We travelled there.*	11	*They improved a lot.*
4	*I looked at Marcus.*	12	*I received a letter.*
5	*Juan reminded us.*	13	*Frank repeated it.*
6	*I watched the TV.*	14	*I started the car.*
7	*Sue asked me.*	15	*June closed the door.*
8	*They changed it.*		

used to

5

b True: 'It's true that people don't queue much any more.'
c True: 'is unusual these days / my father still does it.'
d True: 'we still get more than enough rain in the other seasons.'
e True: 'men hardly ever wear bowler hats.'
f False: 'A few things don't change .... as if you are mad.'

6

b She used to have short blonde hair.
c She didn't use to have a car.
d She didn't use to have a boyfriend.
e She didn't use to wear smart clothes.
f She used to be unhappy.

still, not any more / longer

7

b Jo used to be shy but she isn't any more.
c Tim and Bob used to play football and they still do.
d Peter used to work for Mrs Warren but he doesn't any longer.
e Sam used to make me laugh and he still does!
f My boyfriend used to buy me chocolates but he doesn't any more.

Listen and read
Frankenstein

8

a)

1 surprised, shocked
2 excited, proud
3 the body of a man

b)

Grammar snack
Articles: first and second mention

9

a)

1 the (line 21): a door in the corner (line 19)
2 the (line 21): a rather unpleasant smell (line 6)
3 the (line 36): a wooden work-table (line 32)
4 the (line 36): a kind of bath (line 31)
5 the (line 37): a clear liquid (line 37)
6 the (line 41): a kind of bath (line 31)
7 the (line 41): a body in the bath (line 41)

b)

2	a	7	a	12	the
3	an	8	the	13	the
4	the	9	a	14	a
5	the	10	the	15	the
6	the	11	the	16	the

Vocabulary
Scientists and technologists

10

a)

2	science	5	engineering
3	medicine	6	architecture
4	psychology	7	geology

b)

1	carries out	5	carries out
2	investigates	6	makes
3	treats, gives	7	takes, analyses
4	draws		

Improve your writing
Spelling of Past Simple forms

11 a)

	-ing form	Past Simple
train	training	trained
plan	planning	planned
look	looking	looked
fax	faxing	faxed
phone	phoning	phoned
offer	offering	offered
travel	travelling	travelled
allow	allowing	allowed

b)

2   enjoyed   6   employed
3   hurried   7   stayed
4   played   8   dried
5   paid   9   applied

Using when / while / as / during / for in stories

12 a)

2   ~~when~~ / ~~as~~ / ~~while~~ / during / for
3   when / as / while / ~~during~~ / for
4   when / as / while / ~~during~~ / ~~for~~
5   when / as / while / ~~during~~ / ~~for~~
6   when / ~~as~~ / ~~while~~ / during / ~~for~~
7   ~~when~~ / ~~as~~ / ~~while~~ / during / ~~for~~

b)

2   while / when / as   6   during
3   While / When / As   7   for
4   for   8   When
5   When

module 3

Comparatives and superlatives

1

2   the biggest   7   quieter
3   the most central   8   the most expensive
4   better   9   more crowded
5   further   10   the most successful
6   friendlier

2

b   The flat is **much / a lot** smaller than the house.
c   The flat is **slightly / a little / a bit** closer to the station than the house.
d   The house is **much / a lot** quieter than the flat.
e   The flat is **much / a lot** cleaner than the house.
f   The furniture in the flat is **much / a lot** worse than the furniture in the house.

Comparative and superlative adverbs
3 a)

2   Could you write more clearly please?
3   Could you drive faster / more quickly please?
4   Could you explain more slowly please?
5   Could you come earlier tomorrow please?
6   Could you ring back later please?
7   Could you stay longer please?

Comparing things in different ways

4

b   The Manor Hotel isn't as expensive as the Park Hotel.
c   Savewell supermarket has more customers a day than Pricerite supermarket.
d   It takes less time to cross the city by bike than by bus.
e   There are fewer trains in the afternoon than in the morning.
f   The furniture in my sister's flat is similar to Tim's.
g   The Guggenheim Museum in New York is different from the Guggenheim Museum in Bilbao.
h   My flat's (exactly) the same as Phil's (flat).

Vocabulary
Places around town

5

A	N	T	I	Q	U	E	S	H	O	P	B
C	A	O	G	R	N	D	B	K	S	G	C
E	R	S	J	A	U	F	Q	I	T	B	O
S	T	A	D	I	U	M	T	L	A	F	N
H	G	L	M	C	K	D	G	R	T	P	C
T	A	X	I	R	A	N	K	N	I	B	E
J	L	P	B	O	E	O	H	A	O	D	R
F	L	O	R	I	S	T	S	C	N	J	T
N	E	E	D	F	R	I	B	M	E	F	H
D	R	Y	C	L	E	A	N	E	R	S	A
G	Y	C	I	A	H	K	A	E	S	G	L
S	H	O	P	P	I	N	G	M	A	L	L

a) and b)

2   • stationers   6   • art gallery
3   • stadium   7   • concert hall
4   • florist's   8   • antique shop
5   • taxi rank   9   • shopping mall

c)

1 *Excuse me, I'm looking for a dry cleaners.*
2 *Is there a stationers near here?*
3 *Excuse me, is this the right way to the stadium?*
4 *Excuse me, I'm looking for a florist's. Are there any near here?*
5 *Excuse me, is there a taxi rank somewhere near here?*
6 *Which way is it to the new art gallery?*
7 *Could you tell me the way to the concert hall, please?*
8 *Is there an antique shop on this street anywhere?*
9 *Is 'The Greens' shopping mall this way?*

Grammar snack

Prepositions of place: *at, in, on*

6

2 in	5 at	8 at	11 on
3 on	6 in	9 in / on	12 in / at
4 in	7 on	10 on / in	

Pronunciation

/ð/ and /θ/

7 a)

/ð/	/θ/
another	theatre
there	thank you
these	third
that	both
brother	through

Improve your writing

Punctuation: capital letters

8

a I'm meeting **P**rofessor Allinton on Tuesday **a**fternoon, aren't I?
b Do you know any good **J**apanese restaurants? Our Managing **D**irector, Mr Hashimoto, is coming over next week.
c *Twenty Thousand Leagues under the Sea* was written by **J**ules **V**erne.
d What are you doing at **E**aster?

Grammar snack

The definite article: places

9 b)

with *the*	without *the*
groups of islands: the Bahamas	single islands: Jamaica
republics or unions of states: the UK	countries: Denmark, Spain
oceans or seas: the Pacific	lakes: Lake Como
rivers: the Yangtze	single mountains: Mount Fuji
mountain ranges: the Alps	cities / towns: Shanghai
	roads / streets / avenues: Broadway, 5th Avenue
	squares: Times Square
	bridges: Brooklyn Bridge
	parks: Central Park
	stations: Grand Central Station
	airports: JFK Airport

c)

2	–
3	–
4	–
5	the
6	the
7	the
8	–

Improve your writing

Postcards

15 a)

Dear Pete and Sarah,

We're having a great time here in the Big Apple.
The weather **is** brilliant – hot and sunny. **We** spent most of today shopping – **there are** fantastic department stores here: **my** credit card's not looking too healthy! **We're** hoping to do some sightseeing tomorrow – 5th Avenue, Times Square, etc. **The** nightlife **is** also incredible ... nobody seems to go to bed!

We'll be back in a couple of weeks,

love Sue and Joe

XXXX

Mr a
3 Par
Leice
Engla

We usually leave out: pronouns (*we, you*, etc.), definite articles (*the*), the verb *to be*. We sometimes leave out possessive adjectives (*my, your*).

b)

Dear Sam and Julie,

(We) arrived here a couple of days ago – (the) hotel (is) small but comfortable, but (the) food (is) not great. (We're) going on a tour of the whole city tomorrow; then (we're) planning to try some typical pasta dishes for dinner. (We) hope (your) family are all well, (we'll) see you in September.

Love Mark and Tim

Sam an
School
Broadu
Glouces
Englan

module 4

Present Perfect Simple and Past Simple

1

2 've already had
3 we've done
4 started
5 formed
6 've spent
7 played
8 didn't start
9 found
10 was
11 helped
12 've agreed

2

b   Carrie's a really close friend – **we've known** each other for ages.
d   Hello, er … sorry, **I've forgotten** your name.
f   Oh, that's a nice watch. How long **have** you had it?
i   I see your team's in the final. **Have** they ever won the cup?
j   We **haven't played** tennis together since the summer.

3

2 've / have been
3 've / have never stayed
4 've / have lived
5 moved
6 've / have met
7 've / have had
8 've / have been
9 was
10 had
11 took
12 's gone / has gone

Present Perfect + *just / yet / already*

4

b   I haven't done my homework yet.
c   They've just got married.
d   Has Mark come out of hospital yet?
e   My brother has just bought a new car.
f   Jane has already sent all her Christmas cards.

5 a)

2 d   3 e   4 f   5 a   6 c
7 b   8 g

for, since and *ago*

6

b   Frankie last went to the dentist six months ago.
c   My brother and I started going jogging a year ago.
d   Jane's been feeling sick since last night.
e   I took two aspirins this morning.
f   Pete's been on a diet for two weeks.
g   I haven't done any exercise for months.
h   We played football all day yesterday.
i   I've been doing aerobics since this time last year.
j   My mother hasn't been feeling well since her operation.

Present Perfect Continuous

7

b   broken
c   's had
d   's been waiting
e   been going
f   's been practising
g   been dieting
h   has decided
i   enjoyed
j   Has everyone finished

Grammar snack
Articles with *school, college*, etc.

8

b   1 – at school
c   2 – to church
d   1 – to court
e   1 – left university
f   1 – at college

Vocabulary
Describing people's appearance

9 a)

Face	Clothes	Build	Hair
He's got a friendly face	He wears casual clothes	He's quite slim	He's going grey
He's got a round face		He's of medium build	His hair's quite wavy
He's got sparkly eyes	He's got good dress sense	He's not very tall	His hair's highlighted
	He wears colourful clothes	He's a bit overweight	He's going bald

b)
1   My uncle Bill's **quite tall**. He's got grey, curly hair and a **round, friendly** (or **friendly, round**) face. He often wears very **colourful clothes** and he always looks quite **smart**.
2   My grandmother's **not very tall** and she's a little **overweight**. She's got a **friendly** face and white **wavy** hair. She's getting a bit old now, but she always wears **smart clothes** and she's got the most beautiful hands I've ever seen.
3   My cousin Jim's 18. He's **of medium build** and not **very tall**. He's got long, **wavy** hair and quite a **pointed** face. He likes wearing **casual** clothes: jeans and t-shirts, usually.

Pronunciation
/ɪ/, /iː/ and /aɪ/

10 a)

2   he's medium build
    /iː/   /ɪ/

3   she's got green eyes
    /iː/   /aɪ/

4   her hair's highlighted
    /aɪ/ /aɪ/

5   she's pretty and very slim
    /ɪ/   /ɪ/

6   she's got a sweet smile
    /iː/   /aɪ/

7   he's kind and rather shy
    /aɪ/   /aɪ/

8   he's much thinner now he's in his teens
    /ɪ/   /iː/

Listen and read
Tom Cruise

11

b   False: as a teenager he wanted to become a priest or a wrestler.
c   False: he played a supporting role.
d   True
e   True
f   True
g   True
h   False: he married Nicole Kidman in 1990.

Improve your writing
Punctuation: commas

12 a)

2   Steve practises his guitar every day, and has guitar lessons twice a week.
3   I don't know much about the Beatles, but I like their music a lot.
4   I like going to rock concerts, but the tickets can be really expensive, so I don't go often.
5   'I thought they were rubbish,' Naomi said as we came out of the concert.
6   There were four members of the group: John, Paul, George and Ringo.
7   Jorge said, 'You can borrow my guitar.'
8   'Come on,' Paddy said, 'or we'll be late.'
9   'I can get tickets for the 12th, 13th, or 15th January.'
10 The music was very loud(,) but quite good.

b)

We sat in the airport till Mother Teresa came in. I felt hot⊙ tired and a bit nervous. I wanted to kiss her when I met her⊙but she didn't let me. She told me about her work in Ethiopia. She and her sisters took care of sick people and homeless children. I wanted to help them and I told her about my music.

Then I said⊙ 'I'll give a concert in India for you.'

'No. God will give us what we need.' She turned to one of the important people nearby.

'I saw two big old palaces in the city⊙' she said. 'Will you give me them for my homeless children?'

'I'm not sure about palaces⊙ but we can find you a house.'

'Two houses⊙' said Mother Teresa.

'Two houses.'

I understood that Mother Teresa could ask for anything (,) and she would get it. She was all goodness. She wanted nothing for herself. Then she took my hand and said⊙ 'I can do something you can't do⊙ and you can do something I can't do⊙ but we both have to do it.'

module 5

will and won't

1

b   won't come
c   'll need to order
d   Will you be
e   won't like
f   will they send
g   'll get
h   'll pass
i   won't take
j   'll agree

going to

2

b   's he going to do
c   I am
d   are going to see
e   I'm not going to think
f   Is she going to marry
g   are they going to build
h   we're not (we aren't)

Present Continuous for future arrangements

3 a)

A   a dentist
B   a university student

b)

2   I'm sorry, he's having the afternoon off,
3   I'm going to a lecture this morning and I'm meeting Daniella for lunch.
4   What are you doing in the afternoon?
5   Well, I'm playing squash until 3.00,
6   Are you doing anything in the evening?

Other ways of talking about the future

4

b   They're due to arrive at about six.
c   Where are you planning to stay?
d   Yes, we're hoping to move next month.
e   I know, she's about to take her driving test.
f   Well, I'm thinking of buying a new car with some of it.
g   Yes, he's determined to win the competition.

Future clauses with if, when, etc.

5

b   6
c   2
d   8
e   1
f   7
g   9
h   5
i   3

6

b   Phone me when you're in Madrid again.
c   Let's stop (now) before it gets dark.
d   I'll give you my phone number after I move house.
e   I'd like to see that film as soon as it comes out.
f   Maurizio hopes to get a job once he leaves university.
g   I'll wait with you until the taxi comes.

Grammar snack
Prepositions of time for the future

7 a)

in	on	at	–
2010 a fortnight a moment three weeks' time a month's time	Saturday night Sunday December 1st my birthday Wednesday evening	midday Christmas lunchtime 7.30	the year after next this time next year next month this time tomorrow next Saturday the day after tomorrow

Pronunciation
/ɜː/, /ɔː/ and /əʊ/

8 b)

1 loan
2 weren't
3 walk
4 bone
5 caught
6 low
7 turn
8 bored
9 won't
10 shirt

Vocabulary
Jobs

9 a) and b)

1 accountant
2 lawyer
3 designer
4 secretary
5 engineer
6 receptionist
7 lecturer
8 architect

Adjectives to describe jobs

10 a)

2 f   3 g   4 e   5 d   6 a   7 b

b)

2 stressful
3 creative
4 challenging
5 tiring
6 rewarding
7 varied

Real life
Formal telephone conversations

11 c)

a   A: *Good afternoon, Henderson Insurance, Pam speaking. How can I help?*
    B: *Good afternoon, could I speak to Mrs Leeson please?*
    A: *Just a moment, I'll put you through.*
    C: *Hello, Mrs Leeson's office, Sandy speaking.*
    B: *Hello, could I speak to Mrs Leeson please?*
    C: *I'll just see if she's available. Can I ask who's calling?*
    B: *Jo Spinelli*
    C: *One moment please (pause). Hello, I'm afraid she's not in the office at the moment. Would you like her to call you back?*
    B: *Yes please.*
    C: *Can I take your number?*
    B: *Yes, it's 4442 123451.*
    C: *Right, I'll get her to call you back as soon as she comes in.*
    B: *Thankyou. Goodbye.*
    C: *Goodbye.*

b   *This is the International School answering service. We're sorry there's no one available to take your call. Please leave your message after the tone. If you would like information about courses, please leave you name and address and we'll send you our brochure. Thankyou. (tone)*

    Yes could you send me information about your English courses for executives, please. My name is Jo Spinelli, that's S-P-I-N-E-L-L-I, and my address is 25C, Via Roma, Florence. Thank you.

Improve your writing
Apostrophes

12

b   This is the boys' bedroom. They're both at school at the moment.
c   It's a nice day, isn't it?
d   Whose is this? I think it's hers.
e   Who's that in reception?
f   The company's lost all its best designers.
g   He's leaving in a year's time.
h   I've got five years' experience in advertising.

module 6

-ed / -ing adjectives

1 a)

2 surprised
3 disappointing
4 embarrassed
5 frightening
6 annoyed
7 depressed

Grammar snack
Prepositions after -ed / -ing adjectives

2 a)

2 about   6 at / by
3 about / in   7 about
4 of   8 by
5 in

b)

2 Stella was surprised at / by his behaviour.
3 Adrian's worried about his job interview.
4 I was really disappointed about missing the party.
5 We're very interested in your suggestions about the project.
6 Henry is really bored with his job.
7 Roy was embarrassed about his big nose.
8 My daughter's frightened of the dark.
9 I'm confused about the reason for the meeting.

The passive

3

b When was the prisoner shot?
c Where are tickets for the concert sold?
d When will the new theatre be built?
e Who was the article written by?
f Why has the plant been moved?
g Where is Portuguese spoken?
h What was Napoleon known as?
i Who was the film directed by?
j How many people have been injured?

4

b was found
c have been stolen
d will ... be held? / are ... being held?
e are not / aren't sold
f Was ... built
g is not / isn't included
h Are ... frozen
i will be / is being repaired
j has not / hasn't been told

5

A 2 – are made; 3 – export; 4 – are worn
B 1 – was; 2 – were written;
3 – was staying / stayed; 4 – will be given
C 1 – has been redesigned; 2 – has been made;
3 – opens / is opened; 4 – come

Vocabulary
Films, TV and newspapers

6 a)

2 war   8 advert
3 cartoon   9 chat show
4 article   10 thriller
5 soap opera   11 game (show)
6 musical   12 science-(fiction)
7 headlines   13 review

Grammar snack
Prepositions for talking about books, films, exhibitions, newspapers, TV and radio

7 a)

Newspapers	Films	TV / Radio
in the sports section **on** page 2 **on** the front / back page **in** an advertisement	**in** a film **in** the first / last scene **at** the beginning / end	**on** TV / the radio **on** CNN / Radio Brussels **in** / **on** a programme **in** / **on** the news

b)

2 He was killed in the last scene.
3 They're on page 65.
4 There's a good film on Channel 4 at 8.30.
5 It's on at the National Gallery.
6 On the radio last night.
7 It's on the back page.
8 I think they're in the entertainments section.
9 He was in *Break or Bust*.

Pronunciation
/f/, /v/ and /w/

8 a)

2 Ken goes swimming every week.
 /w/ /v/ /w/

3 Phone me if you're confused about anything.
 /f/ /f/ /f/

4 I'm terrified of storms, especially when I'm outside.
 /f/ /v/ /w/

5 The weather forecast says it's going to get worse.
 /w/ /f/ /w/

6 Philip drove over 1000 miles last week.
 /f/ /v/ /v/ /w/

7 Don't forget to switch off the photocopier before you leave
 /f/ /w/ /f/ /f/ /f/ /v/
 the office.
 /f/

8 Do you believe in love at first sight?
 /v/ /v/ /f/

9 That film got one of the worst reviews I've ever read.
 /f/ /v/ /w/ /v/ /v/ /v/

10 I've just finished my homework. Can I go out?
 /v/ /f/ /w/

Listen and read
Letters to a TV magazine

9 a)

2 positive 3 negative 4 negative

b)

2	True	4	False	6	False	8	False
3	True	5	True	7	False		

Improve your writing.
Linking ideas without repeating yourself

10 a)

I was really pleased to see that you're repeating the _Girlz'n Boyz show_ on MTV. It's the best music programme around and has probably the most interesting guests on it.

I was really looking forward to last Friday's interview with the _Saffron Girls_ but was very disappointed that you only showed three minutes of it. Why did you decide to cut the rest of the conversation, particularly the part where they were talking about their American tour? Please could you show the whole interview in another show soon.

b)

2	It	5	his	8	they
3	it	6	little boy		
4	programme	7	it		

module 7
Polite requests

1 a)

2 Do you think **you could** ...
3 Would you **help** me / **mind helping** me ...
4 Could **you** pass / Could I **have** ...
5 **Yes, of course / Sure.**
6 Will you **get** ...
7 Do you mind **if** I go ...
8 **Not at all / Sure.** I'm going ...
9 Could you **possibly** ...
10 Would you mind look**ing** ... Would you **look** ...

2 a)

2 Do you think I could borrow your camera?
3 Could you say that again?
4 Would you mind checking this letter?
5 Would you turn the radio down (I can't hear you)?
6 Do you think you could lend me five pounds?
7 Do you mind if I give you my essay / give my essay to you a day late?
8 Could I possibly use your computer?
9 Is it okay if I tell you tomorrow?

Ways of making offers

3

b Shall I get a beer for you?
c Do you want me to try?
d Would you like me to take you to the station?
e I'll lend it to you if you like.
f Do you want me to make you a copy?
g Would you like me to send you our brochure?
h Yes, shall I write it down for you?

will (instant decisions and responses)

4 a)

1 A: The black ones look really nice, Madam. Are they comfortable?
 B: Yes, very – I'll take them.

2 A: I've got a problem with my shower. It isn't working.
 B: I'll send someone up straightaway. Which room is it?

3 A: Could you possibly change my flight to the evening?
 B: I'll just check the computer.

4 A: Hi! Nice to see you. Come in and have a coffee.
 B: Okay, but I won't stay long, I can see you're busy.

5 A: Are you ready to order?
 B: Yes, I'll have the fish.

6 A: Could I speak to Mrs Williams in the Accounts Department?
 B: I'll just see if she's available. Hold on please.

7 A: Is there anything good on TV tonight?
 B: I don't know – I'll have a look in the newspaper.

8 A: How much longer are you going to be in the bathroom?
 B: Okay, okay, I won't be long.

Jazz chant (go)

5 a)

2 go for	5 go out	9 went for	12 went out
3 go round	6 go away	10 went round	13 went away
4 go to bed	7 go swimming	11 went to bed	14 went swimming

Grammar snack
Articles: making generalisations

6

a 1 – Traffic; 2 – the traffic
b 1 – The women, the men; 2 – Men, women
c 1 – the exercise; 2 – Exercise
d 1 – people; 2 – the people
e 1 – music; 2 – The music
f 1 – The poetry; 2 – poetry

Listen and read
Food from other countries

7 a)

	Sun	Maria	Maciej
Breakfast	usually no breakfast, maybe rice and soup served with seaweed in it	cappuccino and cornetto	an open sandwich with ham or cheese or tomatoes in it
Lunch	lunchbox with rice and kimchi in it	sandwich	pierogi ruski
Dinner	kimchi, rice and soup, maybe meat – chicken or pork (with soya sauce)	maybe minestrone soup, fish, tiramisu	maybe kotlet or bigos and bread

Vocabulary
Food and cooking

8

b cauliflower	d garlic	f chop	h fork
c prawn	e spoon	g delicious	i spicy

Pronunciation
Lost letters

9 a)

2 restaurant	5 considered	8 offering	11 marriage
3 vegetable	6 different	9 traditional	12 business
4 international	7 interestingly	10 served	

Improve your writing
Sending and replying to invitations by e-mail

10 a)

1 an invitation to a meeting: C, reply: E
2 a wedding invitation: F, reply: B
3 an invitation to stay for the weekend: A, reply: D

b)
Useful phrases
inviting:
I was wondering if you'd like to come …
Let me know as soon as you can.
Could you possibly come to …
I do hope you can come.

accepting an invitation:
I'd love to come …
Yes, I think I can make it.

refusing an inviataion:
I'm afraid …
I won't be able to come.
What a shame – some other time, perhaps?

module 8

Defining relative clauses

1
someone (who) I work with
the thing (that)

2 a) and b)

1 b … and these are the people who / that were staying in the apartment next door.
2 a This is the balcony where we had breakfast every morning …
   b … and this is the beach which / that was right in front of our apartment.
3 a This is a bar which / that stayed open till three in the morning …
   b … and this is the man who / that owned it.
4 a This is a fish restaurant where we had excellent meals …
   b … and this is a woman whose mother cooked wonderful paella.
5 a This is one day (when) we went on a boat trip …
   b … and these are the men whose boat we borrowed.
6 a This is a market which / that was open every Wednesday …
   b … and this is me wearing a hat (which / that) I bought there.

Prepositions with defining relative clauses

3

b to		f on / with	
c with		g with	
d in		h with	
e to			

Quantifiers (*a few*, *a lot of*, etc.)

4
b 4 c 6 d 7 e 3 f 1 g 2

5 a)

2 '… You've given me a lot **of** good ideas for …'
3 There were too **many** people …
4 …but there's not **much** parking space in the city centre.
5 …but **not** many for the evening one.
6 … but not **enough** salt.
7 'Can I have plenty **of** fruit …'

Grammar snack
Articles with countable and uncountable nouns

6 a)

Countable	Uncountable
guest-house	scenery
journey	accommodation
temperature	travel
price	weather
	money

b)

2 –   3 a   4 the   5 –   6 –   7 a   8 –   9 The   10 a

Vocabulary
Formation of nouns

7 a)

-ment	-sion	-tion
equipment	permission	competition
treatment	persuasion	operation
argument	decision	production
advertisement	revision	explanation
improvement	discussion	

c)

2   advertisement
3   competition
4   persuaded
5   decided
6   equipment

Pronunciation
/ʒ/, /ʃ/, /dʒ/ and /tʃ/

8 a)

2	/tʃ/	5	/ʃ/	8	/dʒ/	11	/tʃ/
3	/ʒ/	6	/dʒ/	9	/ʃ/	12	/ʃ/
4	/ʒ/	7	/tʃ/	10	/ʒ/		

Note: words with 'ss', e.g. *permission*, *discussion*, are pronounced
     with /ʃ/
     words with 's', e.g. *persuasion*, *measure*, are pronounced
     with /ʒ/

Reading

9

b	False	d	True	f	True	h	False
c	False	e	False	g	True		

Improve your writing
Formal and informal styles

10 a)

2   I don't suppose you've found it
3   could you post it
4   let me know how much the postage is
5   I am writing to enquire whether
6   I do hope it has been found
7   I would be grateful if you could send it
8   I will of course pay for postage

module 9

Futures for prediction (*will*, *might*, *may*, etc.)

1

b   Carlos probably won't pass his English exam.
c   We may be late so don't wait for us.
d   Chris isn't likely to get the job.
e   I'll almost certainly do an English course here next year.
f   Teresa might well decide to stay in New York.
g   We'll probably go away this weekend.
h   There are likely to be lots of people on the beach.

2 a)

2   We definitely won't have time to do any sightseeing.
3   It's likely to rain before the end of the day.
4   My friend Mari could be a famous actress one day.
5   My boss almost certainly won't agree to the pay rise.
6   You'll probably recognise my sister when you see her.
7   We aren't likely to get back from the theatre before midnight.
8   Our teacher will almost certainly give us a lot of homework for the weekend.

Hypothetical possibilities with *if*

3 a)

2 a   3 e   4 c   5 f   6 b   7 d   8 g

4 a)   b)

a)		b)	
2	's / is	1	'd / would go
3	'll / will call	2	were
4	's / is	3	spent
		4	worked
		5	wouldn't have

If sentences in social situations

5 a)

2   Is it alright if I use the phone?
3   I'll take a message if he phones.
4   Would anyone mind if I opened a window?
5   I'll give you a lift if you like.
6   That'd be great!
7   I wouldn't drive in this weather if I were you.

Grammar snack
Word order of adverbs (*certainly*, *probably*, *definitely*)

6

b   My aunt almost certainly won't hear the phone.
c   Don't ask Nick about the lecture: he probably wasn't listening.
d   It's 11.00: they've almost certainly missed their train.
e   Stephen definitely doesn't smoke.
f   Don't ring Kate, she probably isn't home yet.
g   Jos definitely didn't take the money: he was with me all day.

Vocabulary
Money verbs and prepositions

7 a)

2	into	6	out of
3	for	7	in
4	for	8	by
5	on	9	in

b)

1 Bob: Each month I **put** about a quarter of my salary **into** the bank, because I'm **saving up for** a holiday in the Bahamas and I'm really trying not to **waste** money **on** stupid things like beer and lottery tickets.

2 Sheila: I don't carry much cash around with me. When I go shopping for food, I usually **pay by** cheque.

3 Katie: My mum **pays for** all my clothes, and she gives me some money every week to **spend on** sweets and magazines.

4 Paul: I don't like **taking** money **out of** a cash dispenser when it's late at night. I know someone who was robbed while he was doing that.

5 Jack: I do a lot of small building jobs for people, so I prefer it if they **pay** me **in** cash. I suppose about three quarters of my customers do this.

6 Maria: Well, my souvenir shop's doing very well at the moment, so I'm planning to **invest** two thirds of the profits **in** another shop.

Improve your writing
Opening a bank account

8 a)

2 a 3 d 4 g 5 c 6 i 7 f 8 b 9 h

Listen and read
Lottery winners

9 b)

2 False: he bought more than one new car.
3 False: he didn't give his daughter any money – he paid her to work for him.
4 False: she says he seemed to lose interest in life.
5 True
6 True
7 False: the husband bought the ticket on his own.
8 True

Pronunciation
/ʌ/

10 a)

stomach luxury rough money enough budget
tongue encourage

c)

2 enough
3 tongue
4 encourage
5 rough
6 stomach
7 money
8 luxury
9 budget

module 10

Past Perfect or Past Simple

1

b was, 'd / had left
c felt, 'd / had had
d 'd / had stopped, got
e was, 'd / had eaten
f met, didn't realise, 'd / had been married
g hadn't seen, felt
h sang, 'd / had never heard
i 'd / had written, posted
j became, 'd / had worked
k 'd / had known, asked

Present Perfect or Past Perfect

2 a)

2 a 3 a 4 b 5 a 6 b 7 b 8 a

Reported statements

3 a)

2 On the weather forecast last night they said it would rain overnight.
3 Stephen's teacher told us he's doing very well at maths / he was doing very well at maths.
4 When I was young my father told me I could be anything I wanted to be!
5 They said on the news this morning that ten people have / had been killed in a bomb attack.
6 600 years ago people thought that the world was flat.
7 I've just been reading an article in *Computer Monthly* which said that people in Brazil use / used the Internet more than anyone.
8 My ex-boyfriend sent me a letter saying that he'd just got married.
9 Wayne Rider, the new tennis star, said that when he was young he practised / he'd practised eight hours every day.

b) 🖭

1 *I'm tired. Jack said ...*
Jack said he was tired.

2 *I live in Rome. Cara told me ...*
Cara told me she lived in Rome.

3 *I'm going to Belgium. Pete said ...*
Pete said he was going to Belgium.

4 *I've been there before. Anna told me ...*
Anna told me she'd been there before.

5 *We had a letter from Paul. My mother said ...*
My mother said they'd had a letter from Paul.

6 *I can't come to the party. Emma told me ...*
Emma told me she couldn't come to the party.

7 *I'll be 20 minutes late for class. Mark said ...*
Mark said he'd be 20 minutes late for class.

8 *I'm meeting Liz for lunch. You said ...*
You said you were meeting Liz for lunch.

Reported questions

4 a)

2 He asked me if I was travelling alone.
3 He asked me if I'd / I had packed my suitcases myself.
4 He asked me if I had any hand luggage.
5 He asked me if I'd / I had got off the plane at the stopover in Amsterdam.
6 He asked me how long I'd / I would be in the country.
7 He asked me where I was going to stay.
8 He asked me how much money I'd / I had brought with me.

say and *tell*

5

b correct
c correct
d Roseanne's father told her /said she should be more polite.
e Danny said he was going to the USA / Danny told me (him, her, etc) that he was going to the USA.
f Tell your brother that you're sorry.
g correct
h Could you tell me / say your name again please?

Vocabulary
Weather phrases

6 a)

2	g	5	b	8	a
3	e	6	d	9	j
4	h	7	i	10	f

b)
2 strong
3 thick
4 boiling
5 slippery
6 stormy
7 pouring
8 frosty
9 deep
10 breeze

Listen and read
Sherlock Holmes

7 a)

1 During the night.
2 Four.

b)
2 False: 'I'm glad it's not raining.'
3 False: a man ran ... towards the house.
4 False: ... impossible to see his face.
5 True
6 True
7 False: Holmes jumped on his back ...

Pronunciation
Connected speech: links between words

8 a)

But before we could move, the man had come outside again. In the light we could see that he had something white under his arm. He looked round to see if anyone was watching him. Then there was a sudden crash as he broke the thing against the wall. He was so busy that he didn't see the three of us coming towards him. Holmes jumped on his back and he fell to the ground heavily. Lestrade and I quickly ran to help Holmes. I had my gun ready and soon it was impossible for the man to escape.

Grammar snack
Definite article for shared knowledge

9

2	the	5	the	8	the
3	the	6	the / a	9	a
4	a	7	a	10	an

Improve your writing
Time expressions for telling stories

10 a)

2	while	6	for	10	in the end
3	when	7	until	11	During
4	for	8	after	12	afterwards
5	Afterwards	9	At first		

b)
2	First	4	Afterwards	6	After
3	at first	5	in the end		

module 11

Obligation and permission

1

b should
c aren't allowed
d are allowed
e can't / mustn't
f ought
g don't have
h mustn't / can't
i can
j shouldn't
k must

2

b SC: Can I book aerobics classes in advance?
c LIB: How long am I allowed to keep books?
d LC: Do I have to take (do, have) a test?
e SC: Should I bring a photo?
f SC: Do I have to join for a whole year?
g LC: How many classes am I allowed to miss?

Obligation and permission in the past

3

a)
K: Were you allowed to take a calculator into the exam?
P: No we weren't.
K: How many questions did you have to answer?
P: We had to do twenty in three hours.

b)
P: Were you allowed to stay up late?
I: Yeah, we could sit by the campfire until midnight.
P: Did you have to get up early?
I: No, we didn't have to get up until 9.

c)
M: Did Francoise have a good time in America?
V: No, she had to work six days a week.
M: That's terrible!
V: And she wasn't allowed to phone us.

must and *have to*

5

b	don't have to	e	didn't have to	h	must
c	had to	f	don't have to		
d	have to	g	mustn't		

make and *let*

6

b	6 – let	d	1 – made	f	3 – let
c	4 – makes	e	7 – let	g	2 – made

Spelling and pronunciation
School / university subjects

7 **a)**

mathematics   geography   biology   physics
chemistry   history   languages   literature
information technology   sociology   psychology
philosophy   physical education   media studies
religious studies   economics

b)

geography   biology   physics   chemistry

history   languages   literature   information technology

sociology   psychology   philosophy   physical education

media studies   religious studies   economics

Vocabulary
Transport: noun + noun

8

b	traffic jam	e	petrol station	h	bus fare
c	taxi rank	f	crash helmet		
d	season ticket	g	speed limit		

Grammar snack
Prepositions of movement

9 **a)**

2 e   3 i   4 h   5 c   6 j   7 g   8 a   9 f   10 b

b)

2	towards	4	through	6	through, across
3	out of	5	past, into	7	round

Grammar snack
-ing forms as nouns

10

b   Buying a gun is quite easy.
c   Parking on the pavement is possible.
d   Wearing shorts in church is forbidden.
e   Living with your parents until you get married is common.
f   Getting a divorce is difficult.
g   Walking alone at night is not / isn't a good idea.
h   Getting married at the age of 14 is permitted.
i   Wearing a crash helmet on a motorbike is not /isn't compulsory.
j   Buying drugs is illegal.

Improve your writing
Linking words

11

2	as a result	5	although	8	therefore
3	What is more	6	for this reason		
4	Despite this	7	Besides		

module 12

could have / *should have* / *would have*

1

2 a   3 c   4 f   5 b   6 d

2

b	would have liked	f	could have had
c	couldn't have run	g	wouldn't have believed
d	shouldn't have listened	h	could have been
e	would have bought	i	should have done

3

b	We could have invited	e	I'd have stayed
c	You should take	f	We couldn't wait
d	I wouldn't have had		

Past sentences with *if*

4

b 8   c 4   d 1   e 7   f 2   g 5   h 6

5 **a)**

b   If you'd worn a jumper you wouldn't be cold.
c   Josh wouldn't have lost his temper if he hadn't been very / so tired.
d   If Sam had done his homework he'd know the answer.
e   If I'd gone / been to my usual hairdresser, my hair wouldn't look so terrible.
f   If I'd done a computer course I'd have a well-paid job.
g   Alice would have got your message if she'd been at home last night.
h   If the store manager hadn't known Ruth's father, he wouldn't have given her the job.

Grammar snack
Verb + object + infinitive

7 a)

2 Jim wanted Juliet to stay.
3 My father taught me to drive last year.
4 The local people advised us not to drink the water.
5 John asked Sarah to get him some aspirin.
6 Toni and Jo persuaded the travel agent to give them a discount.
7 My mother reminded me to lock the back door.
8 We told the children not to touch the computer.
9 Ian advised Martin to go to the police.
10 Todd asked his neighbour not to make so much noise.

Jazz chant
Verbs that describe behaviour and reactions

8 a)

2 to get	7 driving
3 to give	8 having
4 of telling	9 to take
5 to believe	10 discussing
6 on hearing	

Vocabulary
Using the dictionary: revision

9 a)

verb	noun	adjective
● advise	● advice	● advisable
● decide	● decision	● decisive
● ignore	● ignorance	● ignorant
● know	● knowledge	● knowledgeable
● solve	● solution	–

b)

2 uncountable	6 countable
3 different	7 make
4 not silent	8 different
5 to	

c)

2 about	6 some (or nothing)
3 found	7 ignorance
4 ignored	8 to
5 decisive	9 knowledge

Real life
Starting and finishing conversations

10 a)

2 h 3 f 4 i 5 g 6 a 7 b 8 d 9 e

b)

2 How are you? I haven't seen you for ages.
3 Hi, glad you could come.
4 Did you have any problems getting here?
5 I hear you're going to study in Prague.
6 I'm sorry to interrupt but I have to go now.
7 It's getting late.
8 Oh dear, is that the time?
9 I really must rush.

c)

2 Did you have any problems getting here?
3 How are you? I haven't seen you for ages.
4 Hello, I've heard a lot about you.
5 I hear you're going to study in Prague.
6 I'm sorry to interrupt but I have to go now.
7 Oh dear, is that the time? I really must rush.

Improve your writing
A letter to sort out a problem

11 a)

44 Barn Road
Nottingham NS4
May 29th 19-

The Manager
Eurotrips Travel Agent's

Dear Sir/Madam

Several weeks ago I telephoned your office to book a return flight to Mexico City, leaving on July 8th and returning on July 27th. You booked me onto a flight costing £425, which I paid by credit card. A week later, I received my credit card receipt and the ticket, but unfortunately the dates were wrong. I immediately returned the ticket by registered post, with a note explaining the problem. That was 10 days ago, and I have heard nothing from you since then.

As you can imagine, I am very concerned about this because I need to make other arrangements for my trip, which I cannot do until the dates are confirmed. I would therefore be grateful if you could look into this matter immediately.

I look forward to hearing from you.